Buckle Down™

Writing

Level 5

2nd Edition

This book belongs to: *Shamar Chillous*

Buckle Down
Publishing

A Haights Cross Communications ✦ Company

Helping your schoolhouse meet the standards of the statehouse™

Acknowledgments

"The Butterbean Tent," from *Under The Tree* by Elizabeth Madox Roberts, copyright 1922 by B.W. Huebsch, Inc., renewed 1950 by Ivor S. Roberts. Copyright 1930 by Viking Penguin, renewed © 1958 by Ivor S. Roberts & Viking Penguin. Used by permission of Viking Penguin, A division of Penguin Young Readers Group, A Member of Penguin Group (USA) Inc., 345 Hudson St., New York, NY 10014. All rights reserved.

"Se-Quo-Yah" lithograph by John T. Bower is reprinted courtesy of the Library of Congress, Prints and Photographs Division, LC-USZ62-1292.

Every effort has been made by the publisher to locate each owner of the copyrighted material reprinted in this publication and to secure the necessary permissions. If there are any questions regarding the use of these materials, the publisher will take appropriate corrective measures to acknowledge ownership in future publications.

ISBN-10: 0-7836-4989-4
ISBN-13: 978-0-7836-4989-4

2BDUS05WR01   8 9 10

Senior Editor: Brendan Wolfe; Project Editor: Nick Caster; Editor: Mary Hickman-Fernandez; Production Editor: Jennifer Rapp; Cover design: Christina Nantz; Production Director: Jennifer Booth; Art Director: Chris Wolf; Graphic Designers: Scott Hoffman, Kelli Rossetti; Composition: Wyndham Books.

Cover image: © Renee Lynn/Corbis

TABLE OF CONTENTS

To the Teacher:

Standards and Skills codes are listed for each lesson in the table of contents and for each page in the shaded gray bars that run across the tops of the pages in the workbook (see the example at right). These codes identify the Standards and Skills covered on a given page.

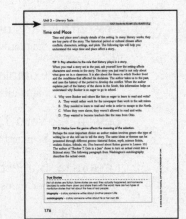

Introduction

You're in Charge

Do you ever daydream? Have you ever pretended you were a rock star? An Olympic gymnast? An astronaut? A professional basketball player? A doctor? When you pretend, you can be anybody you want to be. You can go anywhere you want to go, too. Writing made-up stories is no different. When you're the writer, you can make anything happen.

Visit Distant Galaxies

When you write stories, you can do whatever you can imagine. You can visit distant galaxies, drive racing cars, climb Mount Everest, or even invent a flying TV on wheels.

Other kinds of writing can be fun—and helpful, too. You can share your feelings in an email to your best friend. You can keep a secret journal. You can write a letter to a newspaper. Or you can send a note to your grandmother thanking her for a birthday gift.

Anything you can say, feel, or imagine, you can write about.

You Don't Have to Be J. K. Rowling

Some people get a little scared about writing. They think they can't possibly write anything interesting enough to capture someone else's attention. We can't all be J. K. Rowling or Lois Lowry. But we don't have to be. Each of us has something worthwhile to say. It's all a matter of gaining confidence and finding your own voice.

One way to gain confidence is to create the kind of writing you enjoy reading.

In the list below, circle the types of writing you like to read. If you think of others, add them to the list.

mysteries	poetry
ghost stories	nature articles
sports articles	biographies
news stories	science fiction

_____   _____

_____   _____

_____   _____

Imitating other writers is also a good way to learn to write. On the lines below, write the names of some of your favorite authors and the type of writing each author creates.

_____

_____

_____

_____

Let's Get Started

This workbook will help you improve your writing. It will teach you how to write your best at school and at home.

Everything you do in this book will help you on writing tests, too. These lessons will show you how to organize your ideas so they make sense, how to choose the right words to get across the meaning you want, and how to use details to support your main ideas.

Becoming a better writer is one of the very best things you can do for yourself. You will find that the better you become at writing, the more you'll enjoy it.

And the more you enjoy it, the better you'll become.

Follow the Road to Better Writing

The road to better writing will take you as far as you want to go. There's no limit to how much you can improve as a writer if you continue to read, learn, and practice. If you want to take this journey and become the best writer you can be, it's helpful to have checkpoints along the way. Checkpoints remind you where you've been and show you where you'll go next.

Think of each lesson in this book as a checkpoint. When you have finished all the activities in a lesson and feel that you understand the skills covered, record the date next to the lesson title in the log that follows. Then, have your teacher initial the entry. Before you know it, you'll be that much better at writing!

Date	Writing Checkpoint	Teacher's Initials
_____	Understanding What You Are Writing (Lesson 1)	_____
_____	Thinking of Your Own Ideas (Lesson 2)	_____
_____	Putting Your Ideas on Paper (Lesson 3)	_____
_____	Organizing Your Ideas (Lesson 4)	_____

Date	Writing Checkpoint	Teacher's Initials
_____	Unit 1 Practice: Prewriting	_____
_____	Your Voice and Your Audience (Lesson 5)	_____
_____	Word Choice (Lesson 6)	_____
_____	Sentence Variety (Lesson 7)	_____
_____	Paragraph Connections (Lesson 8)	_____
_____	Unit 2 Practice: Drafting	_____
_____	Being Your Own Editor (Lesson 9)	_____
_____	Parts of Speech (Lesson 10)	_____
_____	Complete Sentences (Lesson 11)	_____
_____	Verb Tenses (Lesson 12)	_____
_____	Subject/Verb Agreement (Lesson 13)	_____
_____	Pronouns (Lesson 14)	_____
_____	Spelling (Lesson 15)	_____
_____	Capitalization (Lesson 16)	_____
_____	Punctuation (Lesson 17)	_____
_____	Finding Errors and Editing (Lesson 18)	_____
_____	Unit 3 Practice: Revising and Editing	_____

Date	Writing Checkpoint	Teacher's Initials
_____	Fictional Narratives (Lesson 19)	_____
_____	Personal Experience Narratives (Lesson 20)	_____
_____	Responding to Literature (Lesson 21)	_____
_____	Informational Writing (Lesson 22)	_____
_____	Writing a Summary (Lesson 23)	_____
_____	Business Letters (Lesson 24)	_____
_____	Letters to the Editor (Lesson 25)	_____
_____	Persuasive Writing (Lesson 26)	_____
_____	Publishing Your Writing (Lesson 27)	_____
_____	Unit 4 Practice: Additional Writing Prompts	_____

Spelling Log

Most people are not terrible spellers. They just misspell the same words over and over. If you have this problem, the best way to overcome it is to learn what words you misspell, and then practice spelling them correctly until you can do it every time.

Whenever you or your teacher find a word that you have misspelled in your work, record that word in the spelling log. Then spell the word correctly four times. The spelling log begins on page 183.

Use the Tips to Help You Learn

In each lesson, you will find a number of tips that give the main points of the lesson. Pay close attention to these tips. They are like signs on the road to becoming a better writer. They will show you the right way to go. A tip will look like this:

 This is what a tip looks like.

Test-Taking Tips

These are some very basic tips to help you do your best on a writing test. Throughout this workbook, you will find specific strategies that will fully explain these basic tips.

 TIP 1: Have a clear understanding of the writing prompt (writing assignment) before you start writing.

Think carefully about the writing assignment before you actually respond. Without a clear understanding of the prompt, your mind (and your pencil) could easily start out in the wrong direction.

 TIP 2: Make a writing plan.

Students who plan their writing have a better chance of receiving a higher score on their writing than students who just dive in and start writing—so get organized *before* you begin.

TIP 3: Stay focused on one topic.

Once you choose your writing topic, stick to it. If your paper begins with one topic, then moves on to another, then another, your lack of focus could result in a low score.

TIP 4: Thoroughly cover the assignment.

This does not mean "write a long paper." The quality of your writing is much more important than the quantity, but make sure your response covers the assignment clearly and completely.

TIP 5: On multiple-choice questions, carefully read *all* the answer choices before selecting your answer.

Sometimes, the first choice on a multiple-choice writing question seems correct, but don't stop there. Carefully read all four choices before selecting the *best* answer.

 TIP 6: On test day, relax. You have the skills to succeed.

After working through the lessons in this book, you'll have all the skills you need to do well on any kind of writing test. So relax and show off your writing skills.

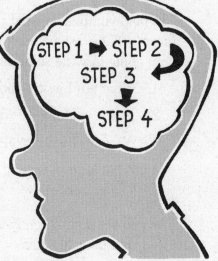

Prewriting

Almost everything we do in life requires planning. Can you imagine what the world would be like if manufacturers sold airplanes, televisions, bicycles, or video game systems without first designing and planning them? If the machines worked at all, it would be a miracle! Writing requires planning, too.

If you want to write as well as you can, you have to start by planning and organizing. First, you have to select a topic to write about. If your teacher assigns you a topic, you need to make sure you understand it. Next, you have to come up with ideas about that topic. Finally, you need to outline and organize your ideas so they make sense. These steps in the writing process are called **prewriting**.

You can develop your writing plan in many ways. This unit will help you organize information about any topic, whether it's one assigned by your teacher or one you have selected yourself.

In This Unit

Understanding What You Are Writing

Thinking of Your Own Ideas

Putting Your Ideas on Paper

Organizing Your Ideas

Lesson 1: Understanding What You Are Writing

Every time you sit down to write something, you must make some choices about *what* you are going to write about and *how* it should be written.

> **TIP 1: Before you start writing, decide what your topic, audience, purpose, and form will be.**

Imagine that your school has a policy stating that students are not to wear hats inside the building. You and your friends decide to send a letter to the principal, Mrs. Hurley, asking that the policy be changed. Your friends have asked you to write the letter.

To help you decide what your topic, audience, purpose, and form will be, ask yourself the following questions whenever you are going to write something:

1. What am I writing about? (Topic)

2. To/for whom am I writing? (Audience)

3. Why am I writing? (Purpose—to persuade, to inform, to entertain, etc.)

4. What kind of writing will this be? (Form—a letter, a report, a summary, a story, etc.)

As you are getting ready to write your letter to Mrs. Hurley, you might answer the four questions like this:

1. What am I writing about?

   <u>a request for a change in the school's "no hats" policy and our reasons</u>

   <u>for wanting it changed</u>

2. To/for whom am I writing?

   <u>the school principal, Mrs. Hurley</u>

3. Why am I writing?

   <u>My friends and I want to persuade the school to change the "no hats"</u>

   <u>policy.</u>

4. What kind of writing will this be?

    a letter

Practice Activity

Directions: Read the prompt below and then answer Numbers 1 through 4.

Imagine that your class is planning a bake sale. You will use the money you earn to buy teddy bears to give to the local police and fire departments. Police and firefighters will give the teddy bears to children who have been frightened by an accident or fire. You have been asked to write an advertisement for your local newspaper telling about your project. This information will let readers know about your bake sale so more people will come and support your cause.

1. What am I writing about? (Topic)

    _____

    _____

2. To/for whom am I writing? (Audience)

    _____

    _____

3. Why am I writing? (Purpose)

    _____

    _____

4. What kind of writing will this be? (Form)

    _____

    _____

Lesson 2: Thinking of Your Own Ideas

Sometimes you will be given a topic to write about. Other times, you will have to come up with your own topic. Either way, it's your job to think of ideas that will make your writing interesting, exciting, convincing, or informative. The more ideas you have, and the better the ideas are, the more they will help you with your writing.

TIP 1: Talk to people about your ideas—and listen to theirs.

To think up new ideas, try talking to other people. You might get together with some classmates to discuss the history papers you each have to write for school. Or maybe you go out for pizza with friends and talk about the basketball game your team just won. Anytime you talk to other people, ideas are passed back and forth. Pay attention to these ideas. They might be useful in your writing.

TIP 2: Interview people or take a survey to get specific information.

When you write to inform or explain, you may find it helpful to interview experts or take a survey to get information. As you think of questions to ask people, remember the **5 Ws** and the **1 H**. These stand for **Who**, **What**, **When**, **Where**, **Why**, and **How**. If you can answer most of these six questions, you will almost always have all the information that you need.

Imagine that you are going to write about stray cats that are taken to the animal shelter and need to be adopted by families.

To whom might you talk if you needed some ideas and information for your paper?

_____

_____

_____

_____

TIP 3: Reading can help you think of ideas for your writing.

It's always a good idea to read as much as you can. It's also important to read many different types of writing, such as fiction and nonfiction books, newspapers, and poems. The more you read, the more knowledge you will gain. And the more knowledge you have, the better prepared you will be for any kind of writing you might have to do.

If you are going to write an informational report, it is important to do some background reading before you start writing. Your research will help you decide what information is important enough to include in your report; it will also help you make sure your facts are correct.

TIP 4: Keep a list of ideas to write about.

Jot down any idea that might be interesting to write about. It doesn't matter if you write your ideas in a special notebook, in the back of this book, or just on a piece of scratch paper. When you read through your list, you might think of other ideas to add.

Practice Activity

Directions: Imagine that you are going to write a short essay about a musical instrument that you would like to play. Then answer the following questions.

1. Think about a few musical instruments you might want to learn to play and why you would choose to play them. List any ideas you have.

_____

_____

_____

_____

_____

_____

2. Talk to the person sitting next to you about the instruments he or she has listed. Find out why he or she would like to play one of these instruments. Then write down any new ideas you have for your own essay.

_____

_____

_____

_____

3. Is there someone you think would be helpful to talk to for your essay? If so, who? What kinds of questions would you ask this person?

_____

_____

_____

_____

4. Is there anything that might be helpful to read before you write your essay? If so, what? How would this be helpful?

_____

_____

_____

_____

Lesson 3: Putting Your Ideas on Paper

So you have a great idea. That's a start, but what comes next? Sometimes when you write down an idea, it will lead to another idea and then another, until you have all you need to start writing. But more often, it takes a little work to turn an idea for a topic into something that you can write about.

Brainstorming

 TIP 1: Brainstorming is a sure way to think of a lot of ideas quickly.

To **brainstorm**, write down as many ideas as you can as fast as you can. If one idea leads to another idea, draw a line to connect the two ideas. Write down any idea that pops into your head, even if it seems silly. This isn't the time to judge whether an idea is good or bad.

TIP 2: When you brainstorm, it's okay if your paper looks messy.

When you brainstorm, don't worry about how your paper looks. Write big, write small. Write upside down if it helps. Circle things, then underline them. Draw a picture. Do whatever works best for you. Many students like **clustering** or **webbing** because it shows how their ideas are connected to each other.

If you were brainstorming about your favorite sports, your cluster might look like the one below.

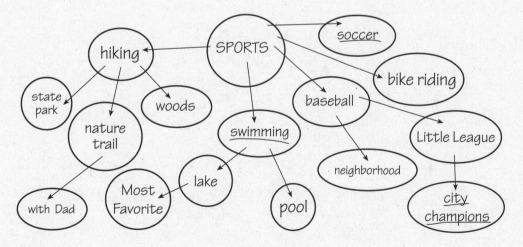

Practice Activity 1

Directions: Answer the four focus questions to help you understand the topic. Then brainstorm in the space that follows.

In an essay for your teacher, describe your favorite movie. Be sure to include details about the fun parts of the movie and the things you did not like as much.

Understanding the Topic:

1. What am I writing about? (Topic)

   _____

2. To/for whom am I writing? (Audience) _____

3. Why am I writing? (Purpose)

   _____

4. What kind of writing will this be? (Form) _____

Brainstorm in the space below.

Freewriting

Sometimes brainstorming isn't enough to get you to the point where you can start writing. When this is the case, you can try **freewriting**.

▷ **TIP 3: The key to freewriting is to never stop writing.**

When you freewrite, start writing about your topic as fast as you can and don't stop. Two or three minutes is usually enough time. Don't worry about spelling, punctuation, capitalization, or grammar. You just want to get your thoughts down on paper.

Here is an example of freewriting on the following topic:

Write an essay telling about your favorite kind of animal.

my favorite is a dog. I have a dog and he is one of my best friends. he goes every place I go and always seems to be happy with me. most other animals aren't as friendly as a dog my cat doesn't ever want to do anything except sleep but I like horses too I can't have a horse in the city but if I ever lived on a farm I would have a horse. some wild animals are favorites of mine, like monkeys and tigers. Sometimes I wish I had a monkey. but a monkey wouldn't make a good pet like Bowser he's a beagle and we do lots of stuff together. Fish and hamsters also make good pets.

There are several ideas in this example of freewriting. Before you could actually write an essay, you would have to pick one idea to write about.

Practice Activity 2

Directions: First, answer the four focus questions about the following topic. Then freewrite about the topic for two or three minutes. Write as fast as you can and record anything about the topic that pops into your mind.

In an essay for your teacher, write about your best friend and tell why he or she is your best friend.

Understanding the Topic:

1. What am I writing about? (Topic)

    _____

2. To/for whom am I writing? (Audience) _____

3. Why am I writing? (Purpose)

    _____

4. What kind of writing will this be? (Form) _____

Freewrite in the space below.

_____

_____

_____

_____

_____

_____

_____

Graphic Organizers

Graphic organizers, such as the web on page 13 and the Venn diagram below, can help you connect your ideas while you are brainstorming or after you have done some freewriting.

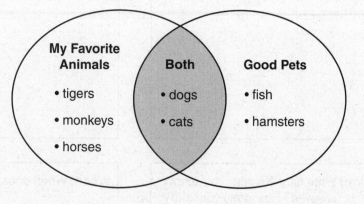

Practice Activity 3

Directions: First, answer the four focus questions about the following topic. Then write answers to the questions in the story map on page 18.

Write a made-up story for your classmates in which a fifth-grader saves his or her school from aliens from outer space.

Understanding the Topic:

1. What am I writing about? (Topic)

    _____

2. To/for whom am I writing? (Audience) _____

3. Why am I writing? (Purpose)

    _____

4. What kind of writing will this be? (Form) _____

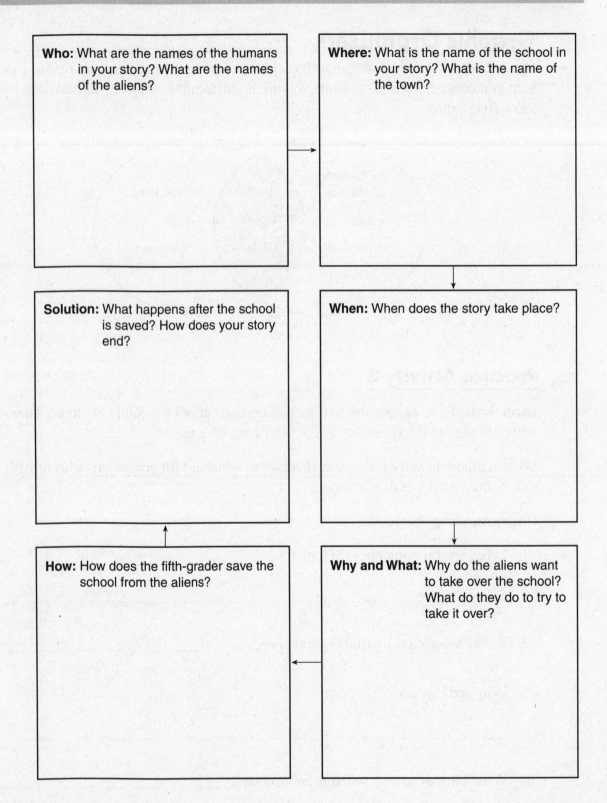

Who: What are the names of the humans in your story? What are the names of the aliens?

Where: What is the name of the school in your story? What is the name of the town?

Solution: What happens after the school is saved? How does your story end?

When: When does the story take place?

How: How does the fifth-grader save the school from the aliens?

Why and What: Why do the aliens want to take over the school? What do they do to try to take it over?

Lesson 4: Organizing Your Ideas

Once you have some ideas for your paper, you need to organize them. To organize your ideas, decide how to present them in an order that will make sense to your audience.

TIP 1: Decide on a main idea.

At this point, you probably have written down a lot of ideas, maybe through brainstorming or freewriting. Now it's time to pick out the most important idea. This will be the **main idea** of your writing. Make sure that your main idea is clear to you. Also, think about how you can explain it so your audience will understand.

Imagine you are going to write a three-page essay about the importance of some form of transportation. Your teacher wants *you* to pick a form of transportation to write about.

A main idea such as "vehicles with motors are important in many ways" is probably too broad for your essay. You wouldn't be able to cover that topic very well in three pages. There are too many different kinds of vehicles with motors, and there are too many ways in which these vehicles are important.

On the other hand, a main idea such as "the shopping cart my dad used at the grocery store last night was important because we had a lot of groceries" is probably too narrow. You could probably write all that you needed in a sentence or two.

A good main idea might be "canoes were important to the Shawnee people in the area that is now Ohio." This topic is narrow enough to cover in three pages, yet it is broad enough that you can write about it for three pages.

What is another main idea you might use to write an essay about the importance of some form of transportation?

_____

_____

TIP 2: Divide your writing into three main parts: the introduction, the body, and the conclusion.

Many kinds of writing—especially essays and reports—follow a basic three-part pattern. First comes the beginning, or **introduction**, in which you tell what your subject is. Next comes the middle, or **body**, in which you explain your subject. And last comes the ending, or **conclusion**, in which you summarize your findings about the subject.

You can compare this type of outline to a field trip to the zoo. Before you leave the classroom, or after you board the bus, your teacher might tell you about the zoo (**the introduction**) and explain what you are going to see. But the main part of your field trip (**the body**) takes place after you arrive at the zoo. When you have completed your visit, you reboard the bus and **conclude** the trip by summarizing what you have seen and discussing what you have learned.

TIP 3: In the introduction, tell your audience what you are going to be writing about.

The introduction lets your audience know what to expect in your essay or report. You should state your main idea in the introduction. You can also mention any other important ideas you are going to develop in the body of your paper. The introduction is usually one paragraph long.

TIP 4: In the body, explain the subject of the writing in detail.

The body is the main part of your essay or report. It should contain important ideas you selected from your brainstorming or freewriting session and enough details to support those ideas. The body varies in length from one paragraph to several pages. It should be long enough to discuss your main idea fully. It is almost always longer than the introduction or conclusion.

TIP 5: In the conclusion, summarize what you have written and connect the end of the writing to the introduction.

The conclusion should offer a short summary of what you have written. It should include the main idea and any other ideas that you have discussed in the body. Try to leave the audience with some new thoughts about the subject of your writing. Like the introduction, the conclusion is usually one paragraph long.

TIP 6: In a narrative story, the conclusion is where you resolve the plot.

Imagine you are writing a mystery about stolen jewels. You probably don't want to reveal who stole the jewels until the very end, right? In a narrative story, you wrap everything up in the conclusion. It's where the detective explains who did it and why, and it's where the jewels are returned to their rightful owner. You'll learn more about organizing a narrative story in Lesson 19.

 TIP 7: Make an outline to help you organize your writing.

In an **outline**, you list the ideas you want to use in each paragraph of your writing. Imagine that your teacher asked each member of the class to write an essay about some form of transportation. You selected the bicycle. After doing some reading about the topic, you brainstormed and did a freewriting exercise. Then you chose the ideas that you wanted to write about. Your outline for the essay might look like the following:

The Introduction
Introduce my topic. Tell that there are four main kinds of bicycles and that they all work the same. Tell about why safety is important for bicycle design and bicycle riders.

The Body
Idea #1: Tell about four main kinds of bicycles:

       mountain bikes

       road bikes

       juvenile bikes

       specialty bikes

Idea #2: Tell how a bicycle works.

Idea #3: Tell about bicycle safety.

The Conclusion
Sum up major ideas. Write a concluding statement that ties the ending to the introduction.

As outlined, this essay will be at least five paragraphs long. Idea #1 may require more than one paragraph because of the amount of information to be covered.

An outline is a great way to organize an essay or report. This method can be very helpful for most other kinds of writing as well.

✏ Practice Activity

Directions: Read the topic below. Then answer the four focus questions to help you understand the topic. Next, use brainstorming or freewriting to generate ideas for your paper. Finally, write an outline in the space provided on page 24.

In an essay you will share with your class, tell about a job you would like to have and why you would enjoy it.

Understanding the Topic:

1. What am I writing about? (Topic)

    _____

    _____

2. To/for whom am I writing? (Audience)

    _____

    _____

3. Why am I writing? (Purpose)

    _____

    _____

4. What kind of writing will this be? (Form)

    _____

    _____

Brainstorm or freewrite in the space below.

Outline your essay in the space below.

_____

_____

_____

_____

_____

_____

_____

_____

_____

_____

_____

_____

_____

_____

_____

_____

Unit 1 Practice: Prewriting

Directions: First, read the following prompt; then use brainstorming or freewriting to generate ideas. Finally, make an outline of your essay on page 26.

In an essay for your science teacher, tell what you think is the most important invention in history. Tell why you think that invention is the most important.

Brainstorm or freewrite in the space below.

Outline your essay in the space below.

_____

_____

_____

_____

_____

_____

_____

_____

_____

_____

_____

_____

_____

_____

_____

_____

_____

UNIT 2

Drafting

In Unit 1, we discussed things you need to think about *before* you write, such as topic, audience, and purpose. Then you learned how to come up with ideas about your topic and how to arrange those ideas using an introduction, a body, and a conclusion.

So, now what?

Unit 2 will help you take the great ideas you come up with and put them on paper using your unique writing "voice." It also will help you choose the best kind of writing for different audiences. Later in the unit, you'll review how to make your writing more interesting by varying your word choice and the way you put together your sentences and paragraphs.

In This Unit

Your Voice and
    Your Audience

Word Choice

Sentence Variety

Paragraph
    Connections

Lesson 5: Your Voice and Your Audience

Think about how you talk. Other people might sound a lot like you, but nobody sounds *exactly* like you. Other people might use many of the same words you do, but nobody uses *all* the same words that you use. When you talk, you have your own **voice**. You also have a voice when you write. Just like your speaking voice, your writing voice is all your own. Nobody else writes exactly like you do.

> **TIP 1: You can use your voice differently for different audiences.**

Do you talk to your friends the same way you talk to your principal? Do you talk to your parents the same way you talk to your dentist? Probably not. You use your voice in different ways when you talk to different people.

Let's say you don't like to eat liver. Here are a few "voices" you might use to show your feelings.

Your polite voice: To a *cook* in the school lunchroom, you might say, "I don't care for liver, thank you."

Your lively voice: To your *mother*, you might say, "Mom, do I have to eat this stuff? I hate liver!"

Your funny voice: What would you say to a *friend*?

_____

_____

You should also be able to use your writing voice in different ways to fit your audience. Sometimes you write just for yourself. When you do this kind of writing, you can use any voice that you want. More often, though, you write for other people. Make sure that the way you use your writing voice fits the audience for whom you are writing.

> **TIP 2: Try writing on the same subject for two different audiences.**

A good way to practice using your writing voice in different ways is to write on the same subject for different audiences.

Practice Activity 1

Directions: Imagine that you were hired to take care of Mrs. Thompson's garden while she and her husband were on vacation. You watered it faithfully every day. You pulled all the weeds as soon as they appeared. One row was very weedy, and you spent more than an hour cleaning it up. You had no idea that those "weeds" were actually Mrs. Thompson's newly sprouted carrots!

For this Practice Activity, you will write two different notes:

1. Write a formal note to Mrs. Thompson telling her that you are sorry about your mistake.

2. Write a note to a cousin or a friend telling about your experience as a gardener.

Directions: Write a note to Mrs. Thompson telling her that you are sorry about your mistake.

Understanding the Topic:

1. What am I writing about? (Topic)

    _____

    _____

2. To/for whom am I writing? (Audience)

    _____

3. Why am I writing? (Purpose)

    _____

    _____

4. What kind of writing will this be? (Form)

    _____

Your note:

_____

_____

_____

_____

_____

_____

_____

Directions: Write a note to a cousin or a friend describing your experience as a gardener.

Understanding the Topic:

5. What am I writing about? (Topic)

    _____

    _____

6. To/for whom am I writing? (Audience)

    _____

7. Why am I writing? (Purpose)

    _____

    _____

8. What kind of writing will this be? (Form)

    _____

Your note:

_____

_____

_____

_____

_____

_____

_____

_____

_____

_____

_____

_____

▷ **TIP 3: You can use your voice differently for different situations.**

The way you use your voice depends not only on your audience, but also on your purpose.

Imagine that your softball team beat your brother's team by 15 runs. What would you say to your brother? Maybe, "Hey, we totally beat you guys! You didn't stand a chance!"

Now imagine that while you were helping your team beat your brother's team in the softball game, you slid into home and accidentally broke your brother's arm. What would you say then? It might be something like, "Hey, the score of the game doesn't matter. I'm just sorry about what happened. Are you okay?"

Practice Activity 2

Directions: Imagine that you are at a summer camp in the mountains and it is time for you to go home. Your favorite cousin is arriving at the camp next week and wants you to stay one more week. You ask your parents if you can stay.

For this Practice Activity, you will write two different letters:

1. Write a letter to your cousin to say that your parents have said that you can stay and you are very excited.

2. Write a letter to your cousin to say that your parents have said that you cannot stay and you are very sad.

Directions: Write a letter to your cousin to say that your parents have said you can stay and that you are very excited. The words you use should show that you are excited. Even if you don't say, "I am excited!" you can choose words that show excitement. Can you think of some now?

Understanding the Topic:

1. What am I writing about? (Topic)

   _____

   _____

2. To/for whom am I writing? (Audience)

   _____

3. Why am I writing? (Purpose)

   _____

   _____

4. What kind of writing will this be? (Form)

   _____

Your letter:

_____

_____

_____

_____

_____

_____

_____

_____

_____

_____

Directions: Write a letter to your cousin to say that your parents have said you cannot stay and that you are very sad. The words you use should show that you are sad. Even if you don't say, "I am sad," you can choose words that show sadness. Can you think of some now?

Understanding the Topic:

5. What am I writing about? (Topic)

_____

_____

6. To/for whom am I writing? (Audience)

_____

7. Why am I writing? (Purpose)

_____

_____

8. What kind of writing will this be? (Form)

_____

Your letter:

_____

_____

_____

_____

_____

_____

_____

_____

_____

_____

Lesson 6: Word Choice

The language you used in the note to Mrs. Thompson about the weeding mistake was probably different from the language in the note to your mom. The second note probably used more relaxed language and more slang. The note to Mrs. Thompson was probably more formal, especially since it was an apology.

▶ **TIP 1:** Writing for an adult audience often requires formal language.

This might not be true for a letter to your favorite uncle, but it applies to many other, more formal situations. Formal writing includes business letters, school reports, sets of directions, and letters to the editor.

▶ **TIP 2:** Sometimes informal language can be effective.

Casual (less formal) language and slang are often used in narrative writing to make stories come alive. You might also use this type of language in notes and e-mails to your friends. Journals and other types of personal writing can use informal language, as well.

▶ **TIP 3:** Think about your audience and your purpose for writing when you are deciding what type of language to use.

Be aware of your audience and your purpose for writing. Use language that feels right for the type of writing you are doing.

Practice Activity 1

Directions: Rewrite the following sentences, changing the casual language or slang into more formal language.

Example: That licorice tastes <u>gross</u>.

<u>   That licorice tastes terrible.   </u>

1. My new basketball is <u>cool</u>.

   _____

2. Mandy is <u>freaking out</u> about losing her coat.

   _____

3. Courtney's party was a <u>blast</u>.

_____

4. Have <u>you guys</u> been to the new swimming pool?

_____

5. <u>Chill</u>, Jason. That's a cat, not a skunk.

_____

TIP 4: It's better to use a more exact word or phrase than a general word or phrase.

People often use very general wording when they speak and write. You might say, "I watched the ball game on TV," instead of saying, "I watched the Denver Broncos play the Indianapolis Colts on ESPN." It's very important to be specific in your writing. Otherwise, your reader might not know what you're talking about.

A general word or phrase usually describes a broad category of things (*a horse, an airplane*). A more exact word or phrase describes one thing in that group (*an Arabian stallion, a Boeing 747*).

Practice Activity 2

Directions: For each general word or phrase that follows, write a more exact word or phrase.

Example: a book

<u>   Charlotte's Web   </u>

1. a car

_____

2. a color

_____

3. a song

_____

4. a restaurant

_____

5. a pet

_____

6. a movie

_____

7. an ice cream

_____

8. a ball

_____

9. a teacher

_____

10. a lake

_____

11. a monster

_____

12. a tree

_____

> **TIP 5: Use similes and metaphors to make your writing more interesting.**

Writers often use comparisons to describe things in new ways. One kind of comparison is called a simile, which uses the words like or as to compare one thing to another. For example, instead of saying, "the storm sounds loud," a simile can describe what the storm sounds like by using a comparison: The storm sounds *like* a roaring train.

Another kind of comparison is called a metaphor. A metaphor compares two things by saying that one thing is another: "The storm *is* a roaring train."

Describing things by making unusual comparisons will help make your writing more interesting and fun to read. So be sure to use your imagination!

Practice Activity 3

Directions: Fill in each blank in the sentences below with a simile or a metaphor.

Example: The baseball flew _like a rocket_____ over the cheering crowd.

1. The clouds are _____ floating in the sky.

2. Shauna's new puppy whined _____ all night long.

3. Meg's fish and turnip soup tasted _____.

4. The old cookies are _____.

5. The fan in the window hummed _____.

6. The spider walked along its web _____.

7. My backpack is _____.

8. Mr. Smith's attic _____.

9. Amy _____ when she gets mad.

Lesson 7: Sentence Variety

What if all sentences were short? What if all sentences started the same way? What if these short questions continued? What if the whole book was filled with them? What if these sentences put you to sleep?

When you write, it's easy to slip into a pattern, creating every sentence in the same way. This is a sure way to bore your audience. Variety gives a freshness to writing and helps keep the reader's attention.

TIP 1: Use connecting words and phrases to make your sentences smoother and more interesting.

One way to create different kinds of sentences in your writing is to use connecting words and phrases. Sometimes just adding a connection, or **transition**, will make your sentences more interesting and easier to follow. Here are some examples of connecting words:

> but, yet, and, or, so, next, then, before, when, although, also, because, besides, however, after, later, on the other hand, finally

Constructing sentences in different ways is not difficult if you think about the possibilities. For example, read the following simple sentences.

> Andy went to the store. He went to Ruby's house.

These sentences make sense, but look at how much smoother they become when connecting words are used to link the ideas.

> Andy went to the store <u>and</u> to Ruby's house.
>
> *Or*
>
> <u>After</u> Andy went to the store, he went to Ruby's house.

TIP 2: There is often more than one way to write a sentence.

In Tip 1, you saw two ways to combine separate sentences.

Now combine the original sentences from Tip 1 into a new sentence of your own.

_____

_____

Imagine that you are writing a short story in which you describe a television belonging to your main character, George. Here's what you want your readers to know:

George's television is big.

George's television is old.

George's television has a small screen.

Here are two ways to combine the sentences into one:

George's big, old television has a small screen.

Although George's old television is big, it has a small screen.

Now write your own sentence about the television.

_____

_____

You get the idea. The important thing to remember is to give your readers some variety. You'll have more fun writing, and your readers will definitely have more fun reading.

 Practice Activity 1

Directions: Combine each set of facts into one sentence. Compare your sentences to those of your classmates.

1. A. I like hamburgers.
   B. I like cheese.
   C. I like tomatoes.

   _____

   _____

   _____

2. A. Brandon plays soccer.
   B. Brandon plays basketball.
   C. Brandon has won many trophies.

_____

_____

_____

3. A. We arrived at the movie.
   B. We bought popcorn.
   C. We sat in the front row.

_____

_____

_____

Practice Activity 2

Directions: Rewrite the following paragraph by using a variety of sentences. Most sentences can be combined to make longer ones. You may want to leave some sentences short to add variety.

Matthew Henson was born in 1867. He was born on a farm in Maryland. He went on many trips with Admiral Robert Peary. Peary was a great Arctic explorer. Henson was Peary's personal assistant. Henson and Peary were the first people to reach the North Pole. Henson traveled with Peary for 20 years. He received many honors for his part in the North Pole expedition. He wrote a book called *A Negro Explorer at the North Pole.* Matthew Henson died in 1955.

_____

_____

_____

Lesson 8: Paragraph Connections

In Lesson 7, you learned how to use connecting words and phrases in sentences to make your writing smoother. You can also use transitions to link paragraphs together and make your ideas clearer to your reader.

> **TIP 1: Each paragraph should focus on one idea.**

Remember that your paper as a whole should focus on one main idea. Each paragraph within your paper should focus on one idea that supports the main idea. If you find yourself drifting towards a new idea, it may be time to move on to a new paragraph.

> **TIP 2: Each paragraph should have a topic sentence.**

A **topic sentence** tells the main idea of a paragraph. Be sure that all of the paragraphs you write have topic sentences or clearly cover a main point.

Imagine that you received the following note from a friend:

> I *do not* want to be at school today! I am tired from staying up to watch a movie last night. My nose is running from the cold I got playing out in the snow without a coat. My foot still hurts from when I stepped on a tack during art class on Tuesday. Oh yeah, and we're having macaroni and cheese for lunch. I *hate* macaroni and cheese!

What is the topic sentence of the note?

_____

_____

▷ **TIP 3: Paragraph transitions lead your audience from one idea to the next.**

As you move from one paragraph to the next, it is important to show your audience how the two paragraphs are related. You can use a transition sentence to do this.

Read the following two paragraphs from an essay about cartoons.

> The word *cartoon* may instantly bring to mind *Scooby-Doo* or Saturday morning TV, but there are many different kinds of cartoons. Cartoons can be found in all sorts of places: advertisements, newspapers, magazines, books, and movies. Cartoons may sell, teach, or comment on something in the news. They may keep us in suspense (Can Batman save Gotham City?), or they might simply make us laugh.
>
> Tony the Tiger wants you to buy a sugary cereal. The Flintstones want you to buy their vitamins. These are just a couple of the cartoon characters that people use to try to make you want to buy things. You can probably think of more.

First, find the main point of each paragraph.

What is the main idea of the first paragraph?

_____

_____

What is the main idea of the second paragraph?

_____

_____

Paragraph 1 introduces the main topic of the essay (different kinds of cartoons), and paragraph 2 supports this topic. However, there is no transition between these paragraphs. The writer skips from one idea to the next. Using a connecting word, phrase, or sentence at the end of the first paragraph or the beginning of the second paragraph would help the reader follow the ideas more easily.

The essay's second paragraph could begin with this sentence:

> Advertisers sometimes use cartoons to sell things.

By adding this sentence to the beginning of the second paragraph, a connection is made between the first and second paragraphs. The reader can see that the second paragraph is building on what came before.

Practice Activity

Directions: Read the following essay about why wolves howl. The transitions between paragraphs have been taken out and listed below. As you read through the essay, write the letter of the correct transition in the numbered blank where you think the sentence belongs.

A. Clearly, wolves use howling to communicate a variety of messages.

B. In fact, there are four main types of howling.

C. In recent years, however, discoveries by wolf experts have begun to change people's attitudes about the meaning of a wolf's howl.

Why Do Wolves Howl?

by Sirius Pitch

Wolves may be among the most misunderstood animals in the world. Stories such as "Little Red Riding Hood," "The Three Little Pigs," and legends of "wolf-men," or werewolves, have given the wolf a bad reputation. Throughout time, people have feared and hated wolves and their eerie, spine-tingling howls.

1. _____

Each wolf has its own unique howl, which helps other wolves in the group, or *pack*, know where it is. Howling can also be heard from a long distance because it has a low pitch and can last a long time. If a wolf is separated from the pack, it will begin howling until its packmates respond.

2. _____

The first type is known as the "lonesome" howl. As mentioned in the previous paragraph, it helps wolves locate each other. The lonesome howl can also be dangerous, however, because it tells wolves from other packs that a single wolf is nearby. Howling too close to another pack can cause wolves to find and attack the lone wolf.

The second type of howl is the "pup" howl. The younger the pup, or baby wolf, the more it seems to love howling. The howl of a pup is shorter and higher in pitch because of the animal's smaller size. By six months of age, however, pups begin traveling with the pack and become more selective with their howling.

The third type of howl is the "confrontational" howl. The leader of the pack, called the *alpha male*, will protect the pack with low, menacing howls when it senses danger or is confronted with wolves from another pack.

The last kind of howl is the famous "chorus" howl, when the whole pack joins in. The chorus howl can create echoes that make six wolves sound like twenty wolves. This kind of howl is good for scaring off rival packs.

3. _____

It is a kind of language that some people believe serves to strengthen the bonds between packmates. Along with gestures such as greeting the pack leader every morning and caring for the young, howling is an important part of wolf society. So, the next time you hear wolves howling, there's no need to be scared: They're probably not talking to you!

Unit 2 Practice: Drafting

Directions: Now it's your turn to use your voice and write your ideas into sentences and paragraphs. Use the outline you made on page 26 to write an essay about what you think is the most important invention in history. Be sure to tell why you think this invention is the most important.

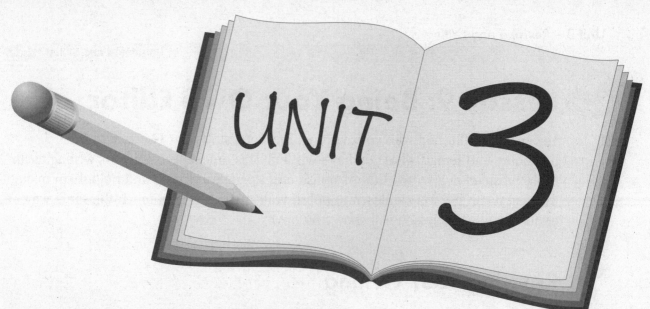

Revising and Editing

Once you've finished your draft, you've put the really hard work behind you. You've come up with ideas, you've organized your thoughts, and you've written your paper. What you have to do next, however, is just as important. You need to **revise** your writing to make sure your ideas are clear and complete. When you revise, you look closely at the way you've presented your topic and supporting ideas, then ask yourself questions such as the following: *Do all the parts fit together well? Is my writing easy to follow? Does my word choice fit my audience and purpose? Does my writing stay focused on the topic?*

You also must check your writing for errors and correct any you find. In other words, you need to **edit**, or "clean up," your draft.

Think of revising and editing as an opportunity. This may be your last chance to polish your work until it shines. You've done your best writing. Now it's time to make your writing sparkle.

Lesson 9: Being Your Own Editor

You have just finished with your writing. But don't stop now. Go back to the beginning and reread what you have written. This time, approach your writing as an **editor** instead of a writer. Editors polish other people's writing and help them make it the best it can be. You can learn to polish your own writing in much the same way an editor would. This lesson will show you how.

Revising Your Writing

TIP 1: Reread your writing to make sure your ideas are clear.

Pretend that you are reading the ideas for the very first time. If you can't understand what you have written, your audience won't be able to understand, either. Your ideas should be presented in a way that makes sense to others. It is also a good idea to read your writing out loud. It will give you a chance to hear if you've left out any words or made any other mistakes.

TIP 2: Add or subtract words, sentences, or paragraphs to make your writing more clear.

Sometimes you will need to add words, sentences, or paragraphs to your writing to describe or explain an idea that may be confusing to your readers.

Other times, you will find unnecessary words or ideas that you have already talked about. You might even see something in your writing that is not clearly related to your topic or your ideas. Get rid of any words, sentences, or paragraphs that aren't related to the main idea of your writing. They will only confuse your readers.

1. Read the following paragraph about learning to ride a bike, and cross out any sentences that don't belong.

    ₁ By some miracle, I learned how to ride a bike when I was in the first grade. ₂ My first-grade teacher was Mr. Rightspell. ₃ My dad was convinced that I could learn to ride my sister Harriet's bike, even though it weighed a ton. ₄ Harriet was in high school, and she stood nearly six feet tall. ₅ She takes me fishing every Saturday. ₆ She had a bicycle that matched her size and weight. ₇ Unfortunately, Harriet's bicycle didn't match me!

2. Write the numbers of any crossed-out sentences on the following line.

_____

Now reread the paragraph and skip the crossed-out sentences. You can see that the writing is clearer and makes more sense.

3. Where would be the best place to add the following sentence to the paragraph?

   I wasn't convinced at all.

   A. after sentence 1
   B. after sentence 3
   C. after sentence 5
   D. after sentence 6

Here's another paragraph from the same essay.

   1 My father covered my knees and arms with heavy padding and took me and the bicycle to a large, empty parking lot at Jefferson Elementary School. 2 He lowered the seat, dropped the handlebars, and attached blocks of wood to the pedals in the large, empty parking lot at the school. 3 At first, he ran alongside, helping me to keep my balance. 4 Then suddenly I was by myself, speeding straight toward the school's vegetable garden.

4. What word or words should be taken out of sentence 2 to improve the paragraph?

_____

▶ **TIP 3: Sometimes you will need to change, combine, or move words, sentences, or paragraphs.**

Sometimes you will find a word, sentence, or paragraph in your writing that needs to be included but just doesn't seem to fit where it is. When this happens, you may need to move that word, sentence, or paragraph to a different place in the writing.

If you do move things around, you might have to add new transitions or change the ones that you already have.

Editing and Proofreading Your Writing

When you've finished revising your writing, you're ready to do the final polishing. Here are some general guidelines for editing and proofreading your work to make your writing the "cleanest" it can be.

 TIP 4: Read each sentence separately from the end to the beginning of your draft.

That's right, read your draft one sentence at a time, from the last sentence to the first. (Don't read each sentence backwards, just read them in reverse order.) This tip may sound strange, but it really works. Reading from the bottom up keeps your thoughts focused on a single sentence at a time. It helps make any errors stand out so you can spot them right away. Once you've finished checking every sentence this way, read the draft again. But this time, read it the regular way—from beginning to end.

TIP 5: Look for one type of mistake at a time.

If you know you have trouble with capitalization, start by checking for capitalization errors. When you have finished, go on to commas, apostrophes, end punctuation, and so on—one type of error at a time. If you try to check for everything at once, you're bound to miss something.

TIP 6: Learn to use editing tools and symbols.

Editors have many tools to help them in their work. The symbols shown below are just some of the tools that editors use.

Use these editor's marks as you look for errors in your writing. The marks will be helpful to you both in this book and in your other writing at school.

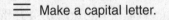

≡	Make a capital letter.
/	Make a small letter.
⌿	Take something out (delete).
∧	Put something in (insert).
⊙	Put in a period.

The following is an example of how to use the editing symbols in your writing:

Life in a New Town

Last June, my D̶ad told me that we were moving from
washington to oregon. I was very upset ^because I had to say goodbye to
my friends. In early August, we packed our s̶t̶u̶f̶f̶ boxes and rode in the
van from seattle to Portland. Our new house was pretty, B̶ut I
thought my new school would be nothing ^like my school in Washington.
I am glad to say that I was wrong! i made new friends the very
first day ⊙ we played baseball at recess and ate together in the
cafeteria. My new town is just as great as my old town.
I̶ ̶a̶m̶ ̶g̶l̶a̶d̶.̶

▷ **TIP 7: Watch out for your writing gremlins.**

Everyone who writes makes mistakes at some time
or another. Quite often, we make one or two kinds
of mistakes over and over again. These are our
"writing gremlins." The rest of the lessons in this
unit will help you identify and avoid common
writing mistakes. You'll do this by reviewing correct
grammar, spelling, punctuation, and capitalization.

Write down one or two types of mistakes that often cause
you problems.

_____

_____

▷ **TIP 8: If you write on a computer, it will be easier to make changes to your work.**

If you save your writing on a computer, you can go back and make changes very
easily. You should always print a copy of each draft to read and make editing marks
on before you actually make any changes.

TIP 9: Use a dictionary or a thesaurus to help you find the right word.

Sometimes when you read your draft, you might find a word that doesn't seem to fit. If you have a dictionary and a thesaurus handy, check to make sure you are using the word correctly. You can also try to find a different word that will work better.

TIP 10: Use a checklist to help you remember what to look for when you are editing your writing.

The following checklist tells some qualities you should look for when you revise and edit.

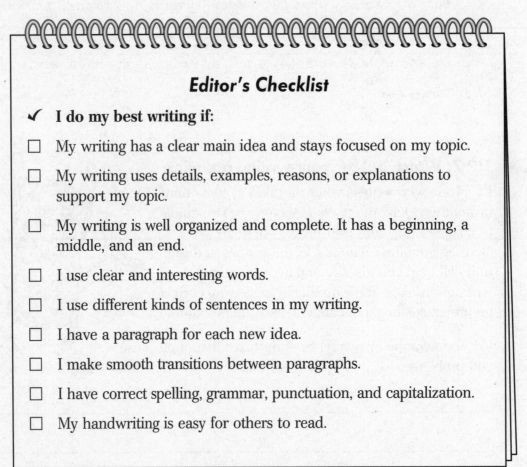

Editor's Checklist

✓ **I do my best writing if:**

☐ My writing has a clear main idea and stays focused on my topic.

☐ My writing uses details, examples, reasons, or explanations to support my topic.

☐ My writing is well organized and complete. It has a beginning, a middle, and an end.

☐ I use clear and interesting words.

☐ I use different kinds of sentences in my writing.

☐ I have a paragraph for each new idea.

☐ I make smooth transitions between paragraphs.

☐ I have correct spelling, grammar, punctuation, and capitalization.

☐ My handwriting is easy for others to read.

✏ Practice Activity

Directions: Read each paragraph and answer the questions that follow.

Paragraph 1

1 Bessie Smith was a popular blues singer during the 1920s and 1930s. 2 Bessie Smith was remarkable for many reasons. 3 She faced hardships as an African-American woman, but she was strong and didn't let anything stop her. 4 In fact, Bessie Smith was the highest-paid African-American entertainer of her time. 5 People all over the country bought her records and people all over the country also lined up to hear her sing.

1. Which of the following is the best way to revise sentences 1 and 2?

    A. Bessie Smith, a popular blues singer during the 1920s and 1930s. Was remarkable for many reasons.

    B. Bessie Smith who was remarkable for many reasons was a popular blues singer during the 1920s and 1930s.

    C. Bessie Smith, a popular blues singer during the 1920s and 1930s, was remarkable for many reasons.

    D. Bessie Smith was a popular blues singer during the 1920s and 1930s, Smith was also remarkable for many reasons.

2. Which of the following is the best way to revise sentence 5?

    A. People all over the country bought her records and lined up to hear her sing.

    B. People all over the country bought her records. People all over the country also lined up to hear her sing.

    C. People all over the country bought her records, also lined up to hear her sing.

    D. The sentence does not need to be revised.

Paragraph 2

6 Bessie Smith was "discovered" by Ma Rainey, a woman who was in charge of a popular musical revue (musical show). 7 Ma Rainey saw Bessie singing in a club and thought that she was very talented. 8 Later in life, Bessie would say that she owed much of her fame and her understanding of the blues to this important mentor. 9 Indeed, Bessie Smith might not have become the "Empress of the Blues" without the encouragement and support of Ma Rainey.

3. Read the following sentence.

   She asked young Bessie if she would like to join the "Rabbit Foot Minstrels," a singing group that toured the nation, and Bessie agreed.

   If you wanted to add this sentence to paragraph 2, where would be the best place to put it?

   A. before sentence 6

   B. before sentence 7

   C. before sentence 8

   D. before sentence 9

Paragraph 3

10 Bessie Smith recorded albums until 1937, when she died in an automobile accident. 11 The world mourned this great loss, but Bessie Smith lives on through her music. 12 She recorded many hit songs, and she was even in a movie called *The St. Louis Blues*. 13 Ida Cox is another famous blues singer whose music remains popular. 14 People around the world still enjoy the powerful songs of Bessie Smith, the "Empress of the Blues."

4. Which sentence does not support the main idea of paragraph 3 and should be deleted?

   A. sentence 10

   B. sentence 11

   C. sentence 12

   D. sentence 13

Lesson 10: Parts of Speech

When an actor plays a part in a movie, he or she acts in ways that show who the character is. In language arts, the **parts of speech** are the different roles that words play in sentences. The ways that the words act define these roles.

 TIP 1: A noun names a person, place, thing, or idea.

Words such as *boy, town, pen, honesty,* and *Mr. Corwin* are nouns.

In most cases, when a noun refers to more than one thing, you can add an *s* to make it plural. the word *boy* becomes *boys, town* becomes *towns,* and *pen* becomes *pens.* An idea, such as honesty or courage, can't be made plural.

 TIP 2: A verb shows action or being.

Words such as *run, watch, be,* and *was* are verbs.

TIP 3: A pronoun takes the place of a noun.

Words such as *he, she, her, it, they, them,* and *us* are pronouns.

 TIP 4: A modifier describes other words. Adjectives describe nouns. Adverbs describe verbs, adjectives, and other adverbs. Many adverbs end with the suffix -ly.

The *extremely tall* boy ran *very quickly.*
(adv.) (adj.)   (adv.) (adv.)

TIP 5: A preposition shows relationships in space or time between a noun (or a pronoun) and certain other words in the sentence.

The words *above, across, after, at, before, for, from, in, inside, of, to, under,* and *with* are prepositions.

We live *across* the street *from* a haunted house.

Let's shoot some hoops *after* dinner.

TIP 6: Conjunctions connect words or phrases to show relationships between ideas.

The words *and, but, for, or, neither, nor,* and *yet* are conjunctions.

> Ben can chew gum *and* juggle oranges at the same time.

> He tried blowing a bubble once, *but* it made him drop the oranges.

TIP 7: An interjection shows feeling.

> *Oh, no!* I guess that was one jelly bean too many!

> *Well*, it seems as if the party's over.

> *Ah*, I see what you mean.

Practice Activity

Directions: For each sentence, circle the part of speech that is given in parentheses.

1. Margie changed her shoes before walking her dog. (Nouns)

2. The dog wagged his tail, waiting for her to play with him. (Verbs)

3. She tried to ignore him, but he started licking Margie's face. (Pronouns)

4. Margie held the dog, and hooked the long leash to his red collar. (Adjectives)

5. He ran quickly down the wide cement driveway. (Adverbs)

6. The excited dog pulled Margie across the lawn and down the street. (Prepositions)

7. Finally, the dog stopped at the pond and Margie sat on the bank. (Conjunction)

8. Wow, I had forgotten how fast you run! (Interjection)

Lesson 11: Complete Sentences

I went to the store I bought some milk. To put on my cereal. Do you like cereal my brother and I like it very much. For breakfast. My favorite food. I don't know what I would do without cereal I guess I would eat more pancakes.

Is there something wrong with this introduction? You can probably understand what the writer is trying to say, but it really doesn't flow very well. This is because all the sentences are either **fragments** or **run-ons**. When you are editing your writing, watch for these and fix them using the following tips.

> **TIP 1:** Every complete sentence must have a subject and a predicate.

The **subject** of a sentence is a noun or pronoun (or a group of words containing a noun or pronoun) that tells who or what the sentence is about. The **predicate** of a sentence is a verb (or a group of words containing a verb) that tells what the subject of the sentence does.

In the following example, the subject of the sentence is <u>Monica</u>. The predicate of the sentence is <u>went to the mall</u>.

<u>Monica</u> <u>went to the mall</u>.
(subject)　(predicate)

As you already learned, a subject can be a group of words containing a noun or a pronoun that tell who or what the sentence is about. In the following example, the subject of the sentence is <u>the man with one green shoe</u>. The predicate of the sentence is <u>ate his dinner with a really big fork</u>.

<u>The man with one green shoe</u> <u>ate his dinner with a really big fork</u>.
　　　　(subject)　　　　　　　　　　　　(predicate)

> **TIP 2:** A fragment is missing either its subject or its predicate.

When a sentence has a subject but no predicate or a predicate but no subject, it is a fragment. The following are examples of fragments.

<u>The woman with three brown gloves</u>. _____
　　　　　(subject)　　　　　　　　　　(no predicate)

What happened to the woman with the gloves?

_____ <u>Laughed at him</u>.
　(no subject)　　　(predicate)

Who laughed at him?

TIP 3: To correct a fragment, add a subject or a predicate.

To make a complete sentence out of a fragment, just add a subject or a predicate, whichever is missing.

<u>The woman with three brown gloves</u> <u>laughed at him</u>.
        (subject)   (predicate)

Practice Activity 1

Directions: Read each of the following fragments. Circle which part of the sentence is missing. Then add your own subject or predicate to make a complete sentence.

1. Is riding her mountain bike.

       SUBJECT   PREDICATE

_____

_____

2. Went to the beach with his family.

       SUBJECT   PREDICATE

_____

_____

3. My favorite poet.

       SUBJECT   PREDICATE

_____

_____

4. Ran three miles yesterday.

       SUBJECT   PREDICATE

_____

_____

5. The red-winged blackbird.

       SUBJECT   PREDICATE

_____

_____

 TIP 4: **A run-on is two complete sentences incorrectly written as one sentence.**

Two or more complete sentences that are jammed together as one sentence without punctuation create a run-on.

> The old moose stood on the road it didn't pay any attention to the cars that were driving by.

Use the following tips to correct run-ons:

TIP 5: **Create two complete sentences.**

One way to correct a run-on is to separate it into two complete sentences.

> The old moose stood on the road. It didn't pay any attention to the cars that were driving by.

TIP 6: **Connect two complete thoughts with a semicolon.**

A **semicolon** (;) can also be used to fix a run-on. A semicolon tells you that the two complete thoughts are closely related. Do not capitalize the first word after a semicolon unless it is a proper noun.

> The old moose stood on the road; it didn't pay any attention to the cars that were driving by.

TIP 7: **Connect two complete thoughts with a comma and a conjunction.**

Another way to connect two complete thoughts is to put in a comma and a conjunction. This is a good way to connect two complete thoughts when the meaning of the conjunction will add something to the sentence. Be careful to check that the conjunction you pick makes sense.

> The old moose stood on the road, but it moved when it saw the park ranger coming.

Practice Activity 2

Directions: Rewrite each of the run-ons correctly by making two complete sentences, adding a semicolon, or adding a comma and a conjunction.

1. I love pizza my sister hates it.

    _____

    _____

2. It stopped raining we should play soccer.

    _____

    _____

3. Margie and her dog love the pond they go there every Saturday.

    _____

    _____

4. I am afraid of heights I don't even like roller coasters.

    _____

    _____

5. Please order three pizzas tonight they're for the slumber party.

    _____

    _____

Lesson 12: Verb Tenses

Yesterday, I will ride my bicycle to Gordon's house, and he joins me to rode in the park.

Although you will probably never make mistakes like the ones above, **verb tense** is a problem for many writers. Verb tense helps readers know when events happen: in the past, present, or future.

TIP 1: Past tense verbs describe actions that have already happened.

Here are some examples of past tense verbs.

Yesterday, we <u>waited</u> patiently. *Or,* Yesterday, we <u>were waiting</u> patiently.

Yesterday, I <u>was</u> tired and hungry.

On the lines below, write two sentences that use past tense verbs.

_____

_____

TIP 2: Present tense verbs describe actions that are happening now.

Here are some examples of present tense verbs.

We <u>wait</u> patiently. *Or,* We <u>are waiting</u> patiently.

I <u>am</u> tired and hungry.

On the lines below, write two sentences that use present tense verbs.

_____

_____

TIP 3: Future tense verbs describe actions that have not yet happened.

Here are some examples of future tense verbs.

Tomorrow, we <u>will wait</u> patiently. *Or,* Tomorrow, we <u>are going to wait</u> patiently.

Tomorrow, I <u>will be</u> tired and hungry.

On the lines below, write two sentences that use future tense verbs.

_____

_____

 Practice Activity 1

Directions: In each sentence below, circle the correct verb.

Example: Baseball used to be Troy's favorite sport, but now he
((likes) / liked / will like) soccer best of all.

1. Jason (writes / wrote / will write) three letters yesterday.

2. Reggie (swim / swam / will swim) in a race next Saturday.

3. Last year we (have / had / will have) over twenty tornadoes touch down in Iowa.

4. Colin Powell (is / was / will be) the highest-ranking U.S. military officer before he retired from the Army in 1993.

5. Right now, chocolate (is / was / will be) my favorite ice cream flavor.

6. I (go / went / will be going) to the pool every day last week.

7. At the moment, Joshua (is drawing / was drawing / will be drawing) a picture of me.

8. My cat (climbs / climbed / will climb) the tallest tree in the neighborhood last summer.

9. My brother, Sebastian, (is / was / will be) in fourth grade next year.

10. Yesterday, I (play / played / will play) my guitar for one hour.

Practice Activity 2

Directions: Rewrite the following paragraph, changing every present tense verb to past tense.

John sits in his bedroom and stares out the window. A moving van backs up to the front door of the house across the street—his best friend Carlos's house. John watches as dressers, beds, chairs, and a table are loaded into the van. There is the sofa that he and Carlos sit on when they play video games. There are the shelves where Carlos keeps his *X-Men* action figures. And there is the blue bike that Carlos rides when they go to the park together. All these things are getting packed into the truck. Carlos really is moving away.

_____

_____

_____

_____

_____

_____

_____

_____

_____

_____

Lesson 13: Subject/Verb Agreement

Three of the main characters in *Cars*—Lightning McQueen, Doc Hudson, and Sally Carrera—are (or is?) on the movie poster I bought.

Subject/verb agreement sounds like a complicated thing, but it's really pretty simple.

TIP 1: A singular subject takes a singular verb.

When you have a singular subject (such as *tree*, *plant*, or *baby*), that word takes a singular verb (such as *grows*).

> The tree grows.   The plant grows.   The baby grows.

TIP 2: A plural subject takes a plural verb.

When you have a plural subject (such as *trees*, *plants*, or *babies*), that word takes a plural verb (such as *grow*).

> The trees grow.   The plants grow.   The babies grow.

Here are some more examples of singular and plural subjects and verbs:

Singular	Plural
I <u>am going</u>	they <u>are going</u>
one <u>is</u>	all <u>are</u>
he <u>runs</u>	they <u>run</u>
the frog <u>jumps</u>	the frogs <u>jump</u>
Susan <u>sings</u>	Susan and Bill <u>sing</u>
the CD <u>plays</u>	the CDs <u>play</u>

TIP 3: Identify the simple subject.

The **simple subject** is the noun or pronoun that the sentence tells about. Other words may describe the subject, but they can be taken out of the sentence without completely changing its meaning. Once you know the simple subject, deciding on the correct verb becomes much easier.

As you read the sentence below, look for the noun or pronoun that is doing or receiving the action.

Example: The smallest dog in the litter of six pups runs faster than the other five.

What noun is the whole sentence describing? _____

Now go back and underline the one-word simple subject in the example sentence above.

Practice Activity

Directions: In each sentence below, underline the simple subject. Then circle the correct verb.

Example: The <u>boys</u> in our club (is /(are)) in fifth grade.

1. My new ballet shoes (make / makes) me want to dance for hours.

2. A group of geese (is / are) called a "gaggle."

3. They (is / are) going to the park to play ultimate frisbee.

4. That swarm of bees (buzz / buzzes) beautifully.

5. All of my fish, except Cleo, (has / have) stripes.

6. Jennifer and Stacy (live / lives) next to each other.

7. The wings on that bat (is / are) huge.

8. Each of the children (like / likes) a different singer.

9. Both dogs (is / are) fast.

10. That pair of jeans (is / are) too short for me.

Lesson 14: Pronouns

While Dexter read Dexter's science book, Dexter sipped hot chocolate from the mug Dexter's sister had given to Dexter for Dexter's birthday.

This sentence sounds kind of odd. That's because it doesn't have any pronouns. A **pronoun** takes the place of a noun such as *Dexter* so that you don't have to use the same word over and over. You probably use pronouns all the time in your writing.

TIP 1: Pronouns take the place of nouns.

Replacing certain nouns with pronouns allows your sentences to have a little variety. Here is how the sentence about Dexter reads when some of the *Dexters* are replaced with pronouns:

> While Dexter read his science book, he sipped hot chocolate from the mug his sister had given to him for his birthday.

TIP 2: A pronoun must agree in gender and number with the noun it replaces.

If the noun you are replacing is singular and masculine, use a pronoun that is singular and masculine.

> Dexter loves science.

becomes

> He loves science.

Here is a list of the personal pronouns:

Singular	Plural
I, me, my, mine	we, us, our, ours
you, your, yours	you, your, yours
he, him, his (masculine)	they, them, their, theirs
she, her, hers (feminine)	
it, its	

TIP 3: Use nominative case pronouns to replace the subject of a sentence.

The nominative case personal pronouns are *I, he, she, it, we,* and *they.* When you are replacing the subject of a sentence, use one of these pronouns.

Replace each underlined subject with a nominative case pronoun.

1. <u>Rita</u> works for the city. _____

2. <u>The band members</u> went running this morning. _____

TIP 4: Use objective case pronouns to replace objects in a sentence.

The objective case personal pronouns are *me, him, her, it, us,* and *them.* When you are replacing a direct object, an indirect object, or the object of a preposition, use one of these pronouns.

Replace the underlined objects with an objective case pronoun.

3. Ron will help <u>his parents</u>. _____ (direct object)

4. Paco gave <u>Ann</u> a big hug. _____ (indirect object)

5. I sit behind <u>Tim</u> at school. _____ (object of preposition *behind*)

TIP 5: Use indefinite pronouns when you are making a general reference to a noun.

Sometimes you will write about someone or something without saying exactly who or what it is. When you do this, you can use indefinite pronouns.

Here is a list of some of the most common indefinite pronouns:

all	any	many	few	most
each	one	everything	anybody	another
either	everyone	someone	anything	nobody
neither	everybody	somebody	anyone	several

Here are some examples of indefinite pronouns being used:

<u>Nobody</u> knows where Donna keeps her diary.

Minnie asked <u>several</u> of us where Donna kept her diary.

Mike said that <u>everything</u> in Donna's diary is written in French.

TIP 6: You can use relative pronouns to combine sentences.

Sometimes you can combine sentences by using a relative pronoun. Relative pronouns can refer to people (*who, whom*), things (*which, what*), or either (*that, whose*).

Here are some examples showing how to combine sentences using relative pronouns.

OK   Meikka has a little brother. Her little brother yells a lot.
BETTER Meikka has a little brother <u>who</u> yells a lot.

OK   My dad has a clown suit. He bought it at a garage sale.
BETTER My dad has a clown suit, <u>which</u> he bought at a garage sale.

OK   Only one of the books sounded interesting. It was the book about the railroads.
BETTER The only book <u>that</u> sounded interesting was the one about the railroads.

Practice Activity

Directions: Circle the correct pronoun for each of the following sentences.

1. Our mother bought (we / us) school supplies last week.

2. Sarah said that (she / her) could dive off the highest rock at the lake.

3. (Neither / Nobody) of us asked for seconds at dinner.

4. Lindsay Lohan is the actress (which / who) plays the teenage daughter.

5. (I / Me) hid in the bushes and scared Roger.

Lesson 15: Spelling

Evin if your speling does not worrie you, make sure that you chek it closly. Poor speling can rooin an otherwise grate paper.

Spelling is not something you should worry about while you brainstorm and organize your ideas. Yet, it is very important in your final draft. You know what you want to say, but will your readers understand you?

There are some general rules that make spelling easier. Knowing these rules will help make your writing the best it can be.

Prefixes

You can add letters to the beginnings of words to make new words. These "add-ons" are called **prefixes**. Here is an example of a root word with a prefix:

        un   +   *sure*   =   *unsure*
     (prefix)   (root word)

By adding *un* to *sure*, the meaning is changed a great deal. Now, instead of meaning sure, the new word means "not sure."

Here are a few more examples of prefixes you should know:

bi   bi + cycle = bicycle

dis   dis + appear = disappear

in   in + exact = inexact

mis   mis + spell = misspell

non   non + sense = nonsense

pre   pre + view = preview

re   re + live = relive

un   un + equal = unequal

Prefixes generally don't change the way you spell a root word.

Suffixes

You can add letters to the ends of words to make new words. These "add-ons" are called **suffixes**. Here is an example of a root word with a suffix:

$$laugh + able = \text{laughable}$$
(root word) (suffix)

Here are a few more examples of suffixes you should know:

ful   thank + ful = thankful

ion   direct + ion = direction

ly   bad + ly = badly

Sometimes suffixes cause spelling problems. In the next few pages, we will review some of the general spelling rules for suffixes.

 TIP 1: Know when you need to change y to i.

Change the *y* to *i* if a consonant comes right before the *y* at the end of a word.

lovely + ness = loveliness

Leave the *y* if a vowel comes right before it at the end of a word.

obey + ed = obeyed

Leave the *y* when adding suffixes that start with *i* (*ing, ion, ible*).

carry + ing = carrying

 Practice Activity 1

Directions: Attach suffixes to the following words.

1. buy + er = _____

2. annoy + ing = _____

3. boy + ish = _____

4. merry + ly = _____

5. envy + ous = _____

6. qualify + ed = _____

Directions: Edit the following sentences by crossing out the misspelled word and writing the correct spelling on the blank provided.

Example: Phoebe's ~~giddyiness~~ may be connected to her fear of heights.

<u>*giddiness*</u> _____

7. Jodi enjoys studiing history.

_____

8. He carried the football more than fifty yards.

_____

9. The party was more enjoiable after Bozo the Clown arrived.

_____

 **TIP 2: Know when you need to drop the silent e before adding a suffix.**

When a suffix begins with a vowel (*able, ible, ion, ing*), drop the silent *e* at the end of the word before adding the suffix.

love + able = lovable

If the suffix begins with a consonant *(ly, ment, ness)*, keep the silent *e*.

love + ly = lovely

If you follow these two guidelines, you will very seldom make a mistake. There are, however, occasional exceptions to these rules. Here are three common examples:

true + ly = truly

knowledge + able = knowledgeable

argue + ment = argument

✎ Practice Activity 2

Directions: Attach the suffixes to the following words.

1. hope + ful = _____

2. adore + able = _____

3. poke + ing = _____

4. type + ing = _____

5. wide + ly = _____

6. shove + ed = _____

7. divide + ed = _____

8. nerve + ous = _____

9. pollute + ed = _____

10. precise + ion = _____

11. arrange + ment = _____

12. communicate + ion = _____

13. wake + ful = _____

14. wide + en = _____

Changing to Plural Forms

Changing singular nouns to plural ones can sometimes create spelling problems. Here are a few tips to help you out.

 TIP 3: Most plurals are made by simply adding *s* to the words.

    cake + s = cakes

    elephant + s = elephants

    airplane + s = airplanes

 TIP 4: Add *es* to words ending in *s*, *ss*, *ch*, *sh*, or *x*.

gas + es = gases	wish + es = wishes
dress + es = dresses	tax + es = taxes
search + es = searches	

 TIP 5: Change *y* to *i* and add *es* when the word ends with a consonant followed by a *y* (*fy*, *gy*, *ly*, *ry*, and so on).

    dairy (change *y* to *i*) = dairi (and add *es*) = dairies

    patty (change *y* to *i*) = patti (and add *es*) = patties

Don't forget that some words change in other ways when they go from singular to plural. For example:

Singular	Plural
man	men
woman	women
child	children
ox	oxen
mouse	mice

Some words do not change at all. For example:

Singular	Plural
fish	fish
deer	deer
sheep	sheep
moose	moose

Practice Activity 3

Directions: Write the plural form of each word.

Example: lamp _lamps_ _____

1. basket _____

2. story _____

3. couch _____

4. dress _____

5. library _____

6. foot _____

7. donkey _____

8. goose _____

9. subway _____

10. calf _____

► TIP 6: Remember the "i before e" rule.

You probably remember the following rule:

> *I* before *E*
> Except after *C*
> Unless sounded as *A*—
> As in *neighbor* and *weigh.*

Put the "*i* before *e*" rule to work in the next Practice Activity.

Practice Activity 4

Directions: Circle the word in parentheses that is spelled correctly.

1. The truck brought in a load of (frieght / freight).

2. I (recieved / received) the call yesterday.

3. My (niece / neice) came to visit for a whole week.

4. Mandy felt happy to make a new (friend / freind).

5. The bedroom (ceiling / cieling) leaks every time it rains.

6. Our cousins took us on a (sleigh / sliegh) last winter.

Homophones

TIP 7: Homophones are words that sound alike but are spelled differently and have different meanings.

There are many homophones in the English language. Here are a few common troublemakers:

by	(past, beyond)	We drove *by* June's house.
buy	(purchase)	Let's *buy* some popcorn.
hear	(one of the five senses)	Did you *hear* that?
here	(a place)	I am over *here*.
it's	(it is)	*It's* not quite dark yet.
its	(belonging to "it")	The tree lost *its* leaves.
their	(belonging to them)	The people forgot *their* things.
they're	(they are)	*They're* probably coming back.
there	(a place)	Don't go in *there*.
to	(in the direction of)	Turn *to* the left.
too	(more than enough, overly) (also)	It is *too* cold to play softball. She wants to go, *too*.
two	(a number)	*Two* plus *two* equals four.

whose	(belonging to whom)	I don't know *whose* gorilla mask this is.
who's	(who is)	*Who's* in charge of the lost-and-found department?
past	(a former time)	She lives in the *past*.
	(beyond)	I went *past* your house last night.
passed	(moved around, overtook)	The car *passed* the truck.
your	(belonging to you)	Is this *your* skateboard?
you're	(you are)	*You're* supposed to call your father.

Write a sentence for each of the following homophones. (Look them up in the dictionary if you need to.)

vain _____

vein _____

vane _____

Words to Know

Study the following words. Some are trickier than others, but all are words you should know how to spell. Check the ones that you think you have trouble with. In the spelling log on page 183, write each checked word four times until you feel confident you could write the word without looking at the correct spelling.

☐ achieve	☐ foreign	☐ observation	☐ thorough
☐ belief	☐ friendliness	☐ partial	☐ thieves
☐ brilliance	☐ heroic	☐ receive	☐ toothache
☐ creative	☐ incident	☐ review	☐ truthful
☐ curiosity	☐ independent	☐ shelves	☐ unique
☐ deceive	☐ justice	☐ sincere	☐ universe
☐ difficulties	☐ kernel	☐ society	☐ volunteer
☐ eastern	☐ ladies	☐ solar	☐ weariness
☐ energy	☐ loaves	☐ strawberry	☐ yellowish
☐ enjoyable	☐ meaningful	☐ technique	☐ zone

Practice Activity 5

Directions: Circle the word in parentheses that best fits in each sentence below.

1. Let's drive (by / buy) the music store to see if it's open. I want to
   (by / buy) a new CD.

2. Can you (hear / here) the speaker from over (hear / here)?

3. If (your / you're) my best friend, you won't mind what I have to say about
   (your / you're) breath.

4. What time is it? My watch says (its / it's) time to buy a new battery.
   (Its / It's) battery is dead.

5. Do you want (to / too) order the cheeseburger pizza, (to / too)?

6. We drove (past / passed) your llama farm after we (past / passed) the
   boomerang factory.

7. (Whose / Who's) going to know (whose / who's) bike it is?

Lesson 16: Capitalization

My Friend denise thought It would be nice to visit washington, d. c., and celebrate the fourth Of july Holiday in the Nation's Capital. Instead, She stayed Home to work on Capitalization.

Can you find the errors in the sentences above? By now, you're probably quite familiar with the rules of capitalization. The following guidelines and examples will help you review the most common problems with capital letters. Under each tip, add your own example on the line provided.

 TIP 1: Capitalize the first letter of the first word of every sentence.

Half an hour is long enough.

_____

 TIP 2: Capitalize proper names, including the names of persons, cities, counties, states, countries, continents, bodies of water, islands, and mountains.

Is Chippewa National Forest near Babbitt, Minnesota?

The United States and Germany are industrial nations.

I want to travel to Rome, Italy, when I visit Europe.

My favorite actress is Hillary Duff.

The Virgin Islands are between the Caribbean Sea and the Atlantic Ocean.

Elizabeth has lived in Los Angeles, Seattle, Helena, and Santa Fe.

She was born in Ada County, Idaho.

Pikes Peak is in the Rocky Mountains.

_____

TIP 3: Capitalize nationalities and languages.

André is <u>F</u>rench.

Rachel is studying <u>R</u>ussian.

I like <u>S</u>wiss cheese.

_____

TIP 4: Capitalize days, months, and holidays.

<u>T</u>hursday, <u>N</u>ovember 24, is <u>T</u>hanksgiving <u>D</u>ay.

_____

TIP 5: Do NOT capitalize seasons.

spring, summer, fall, winter

_____

TIP 6: Capitalize brand names and trademarks.

<u>C</u>heerios, <u>F</u>ord, <u>S</u>ony, <u>K</u>leenex, <u>C</u>oke

_____

TIP 7: Capitalize family relationships if used as part of a proper name.

<u>G</u>randmother <u>W</u>ilson, <u>A</u>unt <u>B</u>ertha, <u>U</u>ncle <u>A</u>lbert, <u>C</u>ousin <u>J</u>ohn

_____

TIP 8: Capitalize *Mom, Dad, Grandpa, Grandma*, and so on, when used in place of a given name.

I'll tell <u>G</u>randma.

I'll see if <u>M</u>other will drive.

Is <u>G</u>randpa here yet?

_____

TIP 9: Do NOT capitalize *mom, dad, grandpa, grandma,* and so on, when used with a possessive (for example: *my, your, his, her*).

I'll tell my grandma.

Let's see if Mario's mother will drive.

Is your grandpa here yet?

TIP 10: Capitalize titles of books, movies, songs, poems, TV programs, magazines, and newspapers.

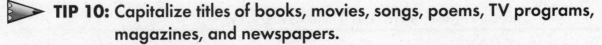

Anne of Green Gables	*Barnyard*	"Jingle Bells"
"Paul Revere's Ride"	*Hannah Montana*	*Readers' Digest*

TIP 11: In titles, Do NOT capitalize a conjunction or an article of three letters or less, unless it is the first or last word (for example: *the, of, on, a, an*).

"The Walrus and the Carpenter"	*Julie of the Wolves*
Number the Stars	*Sports Illustrated for Kids*

TIP 12: Capitalize titles BEFORE people's names but NOT after their names.

General Douglas MacArthur BUT Douglas MacArthur, a general

Pope John Paul BUT John Paul, the pope

Dr. Martha Gray BUT Martha Gray, a doctor

▷ **TIP 13:** Capitalize directions (for example: *north, south, east, west*) ONLY when they designate a region or are part of a proper name.

The storm system will bring showers to the West Coast.

There are many farms in the Midwest.

Vietnam is south of China.

We got on the highway and started driving east.

Practice Activity

Directions: Proofread the following sentences. Draw three lines under each letter that should be capitalized. Then rewrite each sentence using proper capitalization. You may look back at the rules for help.   *circle only*

1. we are going to visit glacier national park this summer.

   _____

   _____

2. have you ever read *raymond and the purple walrus*?

   _____

   _____

3. friday, january 13, is uncle freddy's birthday.

   _____

   _____

4. grandma and grandpa always play golf in jamaica and sail in the caribbean sea without me.

   _____

   _____

5. cindy founded the check mates, a chess club at grover elementary.

_____

_____

6. my cousins live in the southwestern part of colorado.

_____

_____

7. robert's older brother only wears nike or adidas shoes.

_____

_____

8. doctor robinson took his family rafting on the snake river.

_____

_____

9. my all-time favorite book is still *superfudge*.

_____

_____

10. austin is studying history, mathematics, english, science, and french.

_____

_____

Lesson 17: Punctuation

Punctuation marks are like the traffic signs of reading and writing. They tell you when to stop, when to pause, what's coming up next, and so on. Without punctuation, reading and writing would be like driving down a strange road with no signs. You wouldn't know where you were going or what you might see around the next turn.

End Punctuation

End punctuation marks are signals to your readers that a sentence has ended. Learning how to use end punctuation is easy. After all, there are only three end punctuation marks to choose from: a **period** (.), a **question mark** (?), and an **exclamation point** (!). The following tip will help you know when to use each one.

▶ **TIP 1:** Use end punctuation to show what kind of sentence you are writing.

End punctuation tells your readers whether they are reading a question, a statement, or a highly emotional expression.

- **Use a question mark to show that the sentence is asking a question.**

  Do you want to ask a question? Let your reader know this by using a question mark.

  > Are you a good swimmer?

  > Can you come to my party on Saturday?

  > Do you have my basketball shoes?

- **Use an exclamation point to show that the sentence contains great emotion.**

  Exclamation points show that you are excited about what you have to say.

  > Look out for that rattlesnake!

  > I actually shook hands with Ashlee Simpson!

  > School is canceled!

- **Use an exclamation point after an interjection that expresses strong emotion.**

  As you learned in Lesson 10, an **interjection** is a word or brief phrase that expresses emotion. If it is a strong emotion, you can treat it as a separate sentence that ends with an exclamation point.

  Wow!   Ouch!   My goodness!

- **Use a period for every other kind of sentence.**

  Some sentences don't ask a question or show great emotion; they just give you information. These kinds of sentences use a period.

  Kimiko was born in Tokyo, Japan.

  Classes will begin next Tuesday.

  I will have to ask my brother about that.

⚠ **Watch out for indirect questions.** They use a period rather than a question mark.

(They are actually sentences that *tell* about a question but don't *ask* one.)

He asked me if I wanted to go to the movies.

My teacher asked me to name the capital of New Hampshire.

I want to know why we can't have an 11-month vacation.

✏ Practice Activity 1

Directions: Place a period, question mark, or exclamation point at the end of each sentence.

1. Hide quickly ___!___

2. Do you prefer chocolate or vanilla ___?___

3. Mary asked if she could borrow a pencil ___.___

4. This is the quickest way to my laboratory ___.___

5. Run for your lives ___!___

6. Would you like some fries with your ketchup ___?___

Commas

Some people, seem, to think, that, commas, are like salt and pepper, that, they can, be sprinkled, among words any, which way.

In this example, commas aren't used for any purpose. They are just thrown in "any which way." When used correctly, however, commas are hard-working little tools of punctuation that help guide a reader through the writing.

For example, look at how the placement of commas makes a difference in the meaning of the following sentences:

> The boys, say the girls, are the weirdest.

> The boys say the girls are the weirdest.

As you can see, commas are important signals that allow the reader to understand exactly what you are writing. The following rules will help you use commas to make your meaning clear.

 TIP 2: When you list three or more items in a row, put a comma after all but the last item in the series.

> Louise enjoys reading, music, needlepoint, and karate.

 TIP 3: Use commas to set off a street address, city, and state.

(**Note:** There is no comma between the state and the ZIP code.)

> Mail it to 221 Belmont Street, Bellevue, WA 12345.

> Mark lives at 3456 Mississippi Drive, Dubuque, IA 67890.

 TIP 4: Use commas to set off years when used with a month and day.

> Gracie was born May 1, 1986.

> On September 9, 2010, Mr. Griffin will be 58 years old.

 TIP 5: Use commas after the greeting and closing of a friendly letter.

> Dear Omar,   Sincerely yours,

TIP 6: Use commas to help build sentences.

- **Use commas to set off a person's name when you are speaking directly to that person.**

  Rashmi, may I go with you to the beach?

  If I could play ball like you, Ted, I'd try out for the team.

- **Use commas to set off appositives.**

  An **appositive** renames, or explains a word or group of words. If the appositive can be removed without changing the meaning of the sentence, set the appositive off with commas.

  George Washington, <u>our first president</u>, was born in Virginia.

  Glenda, <u>a soprano</u>, has joined the school chorus.

- **Use commas to separate two independent clauses joined by a conjunction.**

  An **independent clause** is a group of words that can stand alone as a sentence. When two independent clauses are joined together with a conjunction, a comma should be placed before the conjunction.

  <u>Cal went to the beach</u>, but <u>he did not get a tan</u>.

  ⚠ When joining two independent clauses, a comma alone won't do the job. Don't forget to add the conjunction.

  Incorrect: Cal went to the beach, he did not get a tan.

- **Often, you will need to separate dependent and independent clauses with a comma.**

  A **dependent clause** is a group of words that has a subject and a verb but cannot stand alone as a sentence. For example, the dependent clause "Although Mike is good at soccer," is not a complete sentence. When the dependent clause comes before the independent clause, you will often need to use a comma between them.

  <u>After the game was over,</u> we went to the pizza restaurant for dinner.

  <u>Because I forgot to get dog food,</u> I had to go back to the store.

  But

  Be sure to give me a call <u>when you get there</u>.

- **Use commas after an introductory phrase (a short phrase that introduces the subject of a sentence).**

  <u>Not wanting to be late</u>, Sarah ran to the bus stop.

  <u>Although small</u>, the suitcase was very heavy.

Practice Activity 2

Directions: Place a comma or commas where they are needed in each sentence.

1. The kittens were named Muffin Twinky Fuzzy and Bruno.

2. Send your letter to Box 191 Grover AL 35601.

3. Henry may I go to the Shakira concert with you?

4. Would you like chocolate pudding or would you rather have butterscotch?

5. To tell the truth I had never tried snowboarding before.

6. Aruna and her family arrived in the United States on June 12 1996.

7. My only cousins Randy and Egbert are coming for a visit.

Colons

Colons are not used nearly as often as commas, but there are times when you need them.

TIP 7: Use a colon between the hour and minutes when writing out time.

School gets out at 3:35 in the afternoon.

TIP 8: Use a colon to introduce the items in a list.

I have several favorite sports: baseball, gymnastics, ice skating, and badminton.

Practice Activity 3

Directions: Add a colon to the following sentences where needed.

1. The game starts at 1 45.

2. Let's go to the beach at 3 30 today.

3. I've got three best friends Tammy, Regina, and Cleo.

4. We ordered four kinds of pizza pepperoni, Hawaiian, vegetarian, and cheese.

Apostrophes

Ji'm's off'ce w's a me'ss. H'e'd pla'c'd that ju'g of a'postr'ophe's on th'e she'lf along w'th the ex'tr'a bot'tle of con'tr'act'ion's. Som'on' h'd sp'll'd them b'th on t'he flo'r. He wo'u'dn't b' abl'e to s'ort the'm out for h'ours!

Apostrophes are used in only two situations: in contractions (such as *isn't*), and in nouns that show ownership (such as *Tom's hat*).

 TIP 9: Use an apostrophe to show the letters missing in a contraction.

A **contraction** is a way of combining two words into one. An apostrophe takes the place of the letter or letters that drop out of the newly formed word.

   you + are = you're

   do + not = don't

   can + not = can't

In this contraction, the apostrophe takes the place of the missing *a* in the word *are*.

 TIP 10: Use an apostrophe with nouns to show ownership.

In English, we add an *s* to most singular words to make them plural (more than one).

   (one) *girl* + *s* = *girls* (more than one)

Adding an apostrophe plus an *s* (*'s*) to a singular word, however, does *not* make the word plural. Instead, it shows that a single thing possesses (has) something else.

   (one) *girl* + *'s* = *girl's* (belonging to one girl)

The following are a few general rules for using apostrophes to show possession. Read the examples given.

- **An apostrophe plus an *s* (*'s*) shows ownership by a singular noun or pronoun.**

   the ballplayer's glove (one ballplayer owns the glove)

   Bess's tuba (Bess owns the tuba)

- **An apostrophe plus an *s* ('*s*) shows ownership for plural nouns that do not end in *s*.**

    the men's hats (the hats of more than one man)

    the mice's nests (the nests of more than one mouse)

- **If a plural word already ends in *s*, just add an apostrophe after the *s*.**

    the boxers' jump ropes (the jump ropes of more than one boxer)

    the teachers' lounge (the lounge of more than one teacher)

    the workers' wages (the wages of more than one worker)

- **Don't use an apostrophe when showing what the word *it* possesses.**

    The leopard lost its spots.

Practice Activity 4

Directions: Combine each set of words into a contraction.

1. we + are = _____

2. I + will = _____

3. is + not = _____

4. they + are = _____

5. can + not = _____

6. that + will = _____

Directions: Change these phrases into possessives.

7. the legs of the centipede

    _____

8. the wings of the bird

    _____

9. the skates of the hockey players

_____

10. the net of the fisherman

_____

11. the horns of the bull

_____

Quotation Marks

May I go with you to fight the dragon, Mom? No! I watched her put on her armor. Please? Not today, I'm afraid, she said. She was halfway out the castle gate. Why not? Because you haven't finished your homework, dear. I'll do it later. No self-respecting dragon will fight a knightling whose homework isn't done. I'll be home soon.

It's hard to read the above paragraph, isn't it? Written conversations can be very confusing without quotation marks. The following tips will help you use quotation marks correctly.

➤ **TIP 11: Use quotation marks to show spoken words.**

The following are a few general rules for using quotation marks to show words spoken in a conversation.

- **Use quotation marks to show the exact words that people are speaking.**

    Use a quotation mark at the beginning of the quoted words and at the end of the quoted words.

    "I'd like you to meet Petunia," Mr. Olankanme said. "Isn't she the cutest little python you ever saw?"

- **Periods and commas always go inside the quotation marks.**

    "I'm not going," Jenny said.

    Mark said, "Neither am I."

- **Question marks and exclamation points almost always go inside the quotation marks in dialogue.**

    "Watch out!" Davian yelled.

    The teacher asked, "Has everyone finished today's homework?"

- **Begin a new paragraph whenever the speaker changes.**

    Marilyn had just gotten a new camera for her birthday and couldn't wait to take a picture. Her brother, Kenny, wasn't exactly her first choice as a subject, but he was close at hand. "Can I take your photo?" she asked.

    "I don't know," Kenny said in that tone he used when he was making fun of her. "Can you?"

    "May I take your photo?" Marilyn asked, correcting her grammar.

    "No! You may not," Kenny said, walking away.

Add two new sentences to the dialogue between Marilyn and Kenny.

_____

_____

_____

_____

 TIP 12: Use quotation marks to set off some titles.

Quotation marks should be put around the titles of poems, short stories, songs, and other shorter written works.

    My favorite poems by Shel Silverstein are "Hector the Collector" and "Backward Bill."

    Paul just wrote a new short story called "My Life as a Short Basketball Player."

    I love the song by Kelly Clarkson called "Hear Me."

Practice Activity 5

Directions: Put quotation marks where they are needed in the following sentences.

1. Where do you want to go, Maria asked, to the mall or the skating rink?

    We can do both, Konako replied, if we hurry.

2. Ouch! Ralph said as he sat on a porcupine.

3. I know the capital of Maine, Gary said. Augusta.

4. How many hot dogs can you eat? Jerry asked.

    Twelve, Isaac said, if I don't eat the buns.

5. Every winter, my father reads the poem Snowbound to the whole family.

6. Lori's brother dances every time he hears the song Ring Around the Rosy.

7. Batgirl won't be able to fight crime with us on Saturday, Robin said. She's going camping with Wonder Woman.

8. I hope Melissa can be our baby-sitter, little Jorge said. She always lets me stay up until nine o'clock.

9. Ur was one of the first cities, the teacher said. It was founded more than 5,000 years ago in what is now the country of Iraq.

10. Has the mail come yet? Warren asked. I'm hoping for an invitation to Sarah's party.

11. Dr. Watson, come here, Sherlock Holmes said to his friend. I need you to read these instructions to me very carefully.

    What kind of experiment are you doing, Holmes? Watson asked.

    I'm making chicken soup, the detective replied.

Lesson 18: Finding Errors and Editing

Okay, you've reviewed and practiced a number of writing skills. You also know how to show a writer what needs to be changed using proofreading marks. Basically, you now have all the tools you need to revise and edit your own writing.

But wait a minute. What if your friend George asks you to read over his essay about the history of peanut butter? Should you tell him he's out of luck because you only know how to improve and fix errors in your own writing?

Of course not! Everything that you've learned so far in this unit can be used to help out your friends and classmates. When you share your writing, you and a classmate switch papers and then edit the other's work. In the end, everybody wins because this will make both your papers stronger. Just remember to be polite, be honest, and be thorough.

The following passages are first drafts that need to be edited. Read each passage and, in the questions that follow, decide how best to make improvements.

Miguel is in fifth grade. His teacher asked him and his classmates to each write about something exciting that happened during the school year. Miguel chose to write about the class field trip to the state fair. Read Miguel's paper and think about how you would help him improve it. Then answer the questions that follow.

Our Trip to the Fair

(1) We've done a lot of cool things this year, but the most exciting event is our trip to the state fair. (2) My friend James and I couldn't wait to see the farm animals, try the delicious food, and ride the giant Ferris wheel.

(3) When we arrived at the fair, our teacher told us to stay together at all times. (4) Everyone loved the soft bunnies and the playful goats. (5) One of the workers in the tent even let me feed an apple to a hoarse.

(6) We had a hard time deciding which food stands at lunchtime to visit. (7) James said, "There's so much that looks good!" (8) I finally decided to have a frozen lemonade and a corn dog. (9) I don't like corn on the cob because it gets stuck in my teeth. (10) James had a chicken sandwich and a funnel cake, which he shared with me.

(11) After we finished lunch, we visited the tents where people were selling their own inventions. (12) Mrs. Davis my teacher bought a pen that could write in twelve different colors. (13) There was a friendly woman at one of the booths. (14) She showed us a really cool machine that pressed pennies into different shapes. (15) We all had a lot of fun seeing the inventions, but the best part of the trip was yet to come.

(16) Mrs. Davis said we could each go on two rides. (17) There were almost too many to choose from! (18) James and I stuck to our plan and went on the giant Ferris wheel. (19) Then in the bumper cars, which was a blast.

(20) Everyone was sad when it was time to leave the fair. (21) We all had a wonderful time. (22) I'm already planning to go back next year.

1. What change, if any, should be made in sentence 1?

   A. Change *but* to *except.*
   B. Change *is* to *was.*
   C. Change *state* to *State.*
   D. Make no change.

2. What change, if any, should be made in sentence 3?

   A. Take out the comma after *fair.*
   B. Change *our* to *are.*
   C. Change *telled* to *told.*
   D. Make no change.

3. Which sentence could best be added after sentence 3?

   A. We weren't sure which exhibit we wanted to see first.
   B. The first thing we did was visit the animal tents.
   C. Some of the students wanted to go on the rides right away.
   D. It took about an hour to get from our school to the fair.

4. What change, if any, should be made in sentence 5?

    A. Change *workers* to *worker's.*

    B. Add a comma after *tent.*

    C. Change *hoarse* to *horse.*

    D. Make no change.

5. What is the best way to rewrite sentence 6?

    A. At lunchtime, we had a hard time deciding which food stands to visit.

    B. To decide which food stands to visit at lunchtime was hard.

    C. Visiting food stands at lunchtime, it was hard to decide.

    D. We at lunchtime had a hard time deciding which food stands to visit.

6. What change, if any, should be made in sentence 12?

    A. Add a comma after *Davis* and after *teacher.*

    B. Change *bought* to *buyed.*

    C. Add a comma after *pen.*

    D. Make no change.

7. What is the best way to combine sentences 13 and 14?

    A. There was a really cool machine that pressed pennies into different shapes at one of the booths, it was shown by a friendly woman.

    B. A friendly woman at one of the booths, she showed us a really cool machine that pressed pennies into different shapes.

    C. At one of the booths was a friendly woman and she showed us a really cool machine that pressed pennies into different shapes.

    D. A friendly woman at one of the booths showed us a really cool machine that pressed pennies into different shapes.

8. Which of the following is not a complete sentence?

    A. sentence 4

    B. sentence 15

    C. sentence 19

    D. sentence 21

9. What change, if any, should be made in sentence 22?

    A. Change *I'm* to *Im.*

    B. Change *already* to *all ready.*

    C. Change the period after *year* to a question mark.

    D. Make no change.

10. Which sentence does not belong in this paper?

    A. sentence 2

    B. sentence 9

    C. sentence 16

    D. sentence 21

Gwen is in fifth grade. She has written a paper about her favorite book. A draft of her paper appears below. Read Gwen's paper and think about how you would help her to improve it. Then answer the questions that follow.

The Mysterious Statue

(1) What if you just *had* to get away from your family for a while?

(2) What if you decided to hide out for a week in a museum with your little

brother? (3) What if you discovered an amazing secret that you didn't have

to share with anyone. (4) These are just a few of the things that happen to

the main character in *From the Mixed-up Files of Mrs. Basil E. Frankweiler* by

E. L. Konigsburg.

(5) Claudia Kincaid is almost twelve years old. (6) And very unhappy with

her life. (7) She is upset that her Brothers always get away with everything,

bored with being a straight-A student all the time, and concerned that she

gets no respect from anyone.

(8) She decides to run away and try to make herself *different* somehow.

(9) She talks her younger brother Jamie into going with her. (10) They decide

to live in the Metropolitan Museum of Art. (11) Claudia and Jamie spend

they're days learning about all the museum's galleries. (12) At night, they

bathe in the museum's gigantic fountain, yet they sleep in a 400-year-old bed.

(13) One day, a new statue is displayed in the museum. (14) Nobody

knows who made the statue, but some people think it was Michelangelo

Buonarroti, one of the most famous artists of all time. (15) My favorite artist

is Leonardo da Vinci. (16) Claudia thinks the statue is the most beautiful

thing she has ever seen. (17) She decides to find out for sure who made it.

(18) When her research tells her nothing, Claudia convinces Jamie that they

should visit Mrs. Basil E. Frankweiler, the woman who sold the statue to the

museum.

(19) At Mrs. Frankweiler's house, Claudia and Jamie learns something

special about the mysterious statue. (20) Also learns something special about

herself. (21) She learns that having a special secret is enough to make her

different, and she is ready to return home.

(22) I know what it's like to want to be *different*. (23) I'm not saying I

want to run away from home, but the adventures that Claudia has sound

pretty cool.

11. What change, if any, should be made in sentence 3?
   A. Change *amazing* to *amazeing*.
   B. Add a comma after *secret*.
   C. Change the period after *anyone* to a question mark.
   D. Make no change.

12. What is the best way to combine sentences 5 and 6?

   A. Claudia Kincaid is almost twelve years old; very unhappy with her life.

   B. Almost twelve years old, and Claudia Kincaid is very unhappy with her life.

   C. Although she is very unhappy with her life, Claudia Kincaid is almost twelve years old.

   D. Claudia Kincaid is almost twelve years old, and she is very unhappy with her life.

13. What change, if any, should be made in sentence 7?

   A. Change *bored* to *boring*.

   B. Change *Brothers* to *brothers*.

   C. Change *gets* to *don't got*.

   D. Make no change.

14. What change, if any, should be made in sentence 11?

   A. Change *they're* to *their*.

   B. Change *learning* to *learnning*.

   C. Change *museum's* to *museums'*.

   D. Make no change.

15. What is the best way to rewrite sentence 12?

   A. They bathe at night in the museum's gigantic fountain, yet they also sleep in a 400-year-old bed.

   B. In the museum's gigantic fountain they bathe, yet in a 400-year-old bed they sleep, at night.

   C. At night, they bathe in the museum's gigantic fountain, and they sleep in a 400-year-old bed.

   D. At night, they bathe in the museum's gigantic fountain but they sleep in a 400-year-old bed.

16. What change, if any, should be made in sentence 14?

    A. Change *knows* to *know.*

    B. Change *Buonarroti* to *buonarroti.*

    C. Change *artists* to *artist.*

    D. Make no change.

17. What change, if any, should be made in sentence 19?

    A. Change *At* to *After.*

    B. Change *Mrs. Frankweiler's* to *hers.*

    C. Change *learns* to *learn.*

    D. Make no change.

18. Which of the following is not a complete sentence?

    A. sentence 2

    B. sentence 9

    C. sentence 20

    D. sentence 22

19. Which sentence would be the best to add before sentence 22 to introduce the ideas of the last paragraph (sentences 22 and 23)?

    A. I like this book a lot because Claudia reminds me of me.

    B. I've been to a museum before.

    C. Mrs. Frankweiler seems like a crazy old woman.

    D. Claudia and Jamie's parents are probably glad to see them.

20. Which sentence does not belong in the paper?

    A. sentence 4

    B. sentence 8

    C. sentence 12

    D. sentence 15

Owen is in fifth grade. His teacher has asked him to write a report about a person from the "Old West." Read Owen's report and think about the corrections and improvements he should make. Then answer the questions that follow.

Nat Love

(1) Nat Love was born a slave in June of 1854 on Davidson County, Tennessee. (2) In 1869, when Nat was 15 years old his father died. (3) The Civil War was over, and Nat was free. (4) He left Tennessee and headed for Dodge City, Kansas, where he find work on cattle drives earning $7.50 a week.

(5) This African-American cowboy worked cattle drives for nearly twenty years, traveling across the Old West and parts of Mexico. (6) He was known for his skill in handling horses and moving cattle. (7) Nat, was also an expert, which he explains in his autobiography about, at reading cattle brands.

(8) In 1876, Nat headed north to Deadwood, South Dakota. (9) He went to Deadwood, South Dakota, to enter a cowboy competition. (10) He was the winner of every event! (11) He roped, threw, saddled, bridled, and mounted a wild mustang (wild horse) in nine minutes. (12) His closest competitor took more than 14 minutes.

(13) From a distance of 250 yards, he hit 15 bull's-eyes with 15 shots. (14) The crowd and his fellow cowboys were so impressed that they gived him a nickname that would follow him where ever he went. (15) From that day on, Nat Love was known as "Deadwood Dick."

(16) Later in their life, Nat would write *The Life and Adventures of Nat Love, Better Known in the Cattle Country as Deadwood Dick.* (17) In the book, Nat tells tales about Bat Masterson, Buffalo Bill Cody, Jesse James, and Billy the Kid. (18) Like other legends of the Old West, Nat's tales are usually exaggerated. (19) Hard to tell "true adventures" from "tall tales."

(20) Deadwood Dick retired from the trail in 1889. (21) The following year, he was hired as a railroad sleeping car porter by the Pullman Company.

(22) For Nat, life on the *rails* was probably much less exciting than life on the *trails*.

21. What change, if any, should be made in sentence 1?

    A. Change *was* to *is*.
    B. Change *June of 1854* to *June, of 1854,*.
    C. Change *on* to *in*.
    D. Make no change.

22. What is the best way to rewrite sentence 2?

    A. In 1869 when Nat was 15 years old his father died.
    B. In 1869, when Nat was 15 years old, his father died.
    C. In 1869 when Nat was 15 years old, his father died.
    D. In 1869, when Nat was 15 years old, his father, died.

23. What change, if any, should be made in sentence 4?

    A. Change *left* to *leaving*.
    B. Change *headed* to *heading*.
    C. Change *find* to *found*.
    D. Make no change.

24. What is the best way to rewrite sentence 7?

    A. Nat, was also an expert at, which he explains in his autobiography, reading cattle brands.

    B. In his autobiography, which Nat explains, an expert in reading cattle brands he was.

    C. An expert in reading cattle brands, which he explains in his autobiography, Nat was.

    D. Nat was also an expert at reading cattle brands, which he explains in his autobiography.

25. Which is the best way to combine sentences 8 and 9?

    A. In 1876, Nat headed north to Deadwood, South Dakota, and he went to Deadwood, South Dakota to enter a cowboy competition.

    B. In 1876, Nat headed north to Deadwood, South Dakota, where he entered a cowboy competition.

    C. Entering a cowboy competition in 1876, Nat headed north to Deadwood, South Dakota.

    D. Headed north to Deadwood, South Dakota, Nat entered a cowboy competition, which was in 1876.

26. Which sentence should be added before sentence 13 to introduce the ideas of the fourth paragraph (sentences 13–15)?

    A. Nat then moved on to the marksmanship competition.

    B. Nat looked very sharp in his new western-style hat.

    C. Nat seemed to be very unhappy with his nine-minute time.

    D. Nat eventually became a porter on a railroad Pullman car.

27. What change, if any, should be made in sentence 14?

    A. Add a comma after *impressed*.

    B. Change *gived* to *gave*.

    C. Change *follow* to *followed*.

    D. Make no change.

28. What change, if any, should be made in sentence 16?

    A. Change *Later* to *After*.

    B. Change the comma after *life* to a colon.

    C. Change *their* to *his*.

    D. Make no change.

29. What change, if any, should be made in sentence 17?

    A. Change *tells* to *tell*.

    B. Change *tales* to *tails*.

    C. Remove the comma after the word *Cody*.

    D. Make no change.

30. Which of the following is not a complete sentence?

    A. sentence 17

    B. sentence 18

    C. sentence 19

    D. sentence 20

Unit 3 Practice: Revising and Editing

Directions: Now it's time to revise and edit the draft you worked on in the Unit 2 practice section (pages 47 and 48). Use the following checklist to revise and edit the draft. If other people have read your draft, review their comments. Use the editing symbols you learned in Lesson 9 to make changes in your draft. Then write your final essay neatly on the following pages.

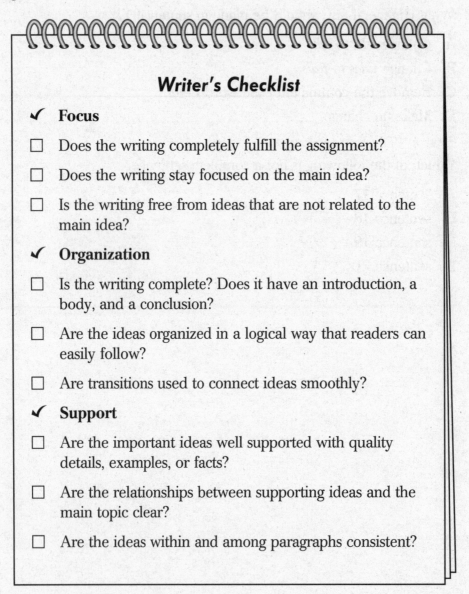

Writer's Checklist

✔ **Focus**

☐ Does the writing completely fulfill the assignment?

☐ Does the writing stay focused on the main idea?

☐ Is the writing free from ideas that are not related to the main idea?

✔ **Organization**

☐ Is the writing complete? Does it have an introduction, a body, and a conclusion?

☐ Are the ideas organized in a logical way that readers can easily follow?

☐ Are transitions used to connect ideas smoothly?

✔ **Support**

☐ Are the important ideas well supported with quality details, examples, or facts?

☐ Are the relationships between supporting ideas and the main topic clear?

☐ Are the ideas within and among paragraphs consistent?

Writer's Checklist (continued)

✔ **Language and Style**

☐ Is the language appropriate for the audience and purpose?

☐ Are the ideas clearly expressed? Are specific, vivid words used to make the writing interesting? Does the writing use appropriate vocabulary?

☐ Does the writing avoid using the same words over and over?

☐ Does the writing use a variety of sentence types?

✔ **Writing Conventions**
(generally agreed-upon ways to write)

☐ Does the writing use correct grammar, including verb usage, noun and pronoun usage, and subject/verb agreement? Is the writing free of fragments and run-ons? (Read each sentence separately—starting with the last sentence.)

☐ Are punctuation marks—end marks, commas, semicolons, colons, apostrophes, and quotation marks—used correctly? (Look for one type of mistake at a time.)

☐ Are words capitalized correctly?

☐ Are words spelled correctly?

☐ Is the writing legible (capable of being read)?

Directions: Write your essay on the following lines.

_____

_____

_____

_____

_____

_____

_____

_____

_____

_____

_____

_____

_____

_____

_____

_____

_____

Writing Applications

Just like playing a new song on the trombone or doing a perfect back dive, good writing takes *practice*. Now that you've learned how to plan, draft, revise, and edit a paper, it's time to bring those skills together and practice what you've learned.

In this unit, you'll learn about several different forms of writing and try out your new skills on each one.

With all this practice, you're sure to become a confident writer, and most important, someone who really enjoys writing.

In This Unit

Fictional Narratives

Personal Experience Narratives

Responding to Literature

Informational Writing

Writing a Summary

Business Letters

Letters to the Editor

Persuasive Writing

Publishing Your Writing

Lesson 19: Fictional Narratives

Science Report: How Soap Cleans

According to most scientists, and my good friend Bob, soap has some kind of magical power. When it is mixed with water, it cleans things. Researchers have known for hundreds of years that soap was originally made by elves in the Black Forest of Germany. Sir Walter Raleigh first brought it to America in 1983 when he visited his mother in Birmingham. Since then, soap has become very popular.
The End

What do you think your teacher would say if you turned in a science report with "made-up" information, like the one above? In many forms of writing—such as summaries, articles, business letters, and reports—you must deal with facts. You can't just make up information and turn it in for a science report or use made-up information in a business letter.

Yet, when you are writing a **fictional narrative**, you can do just that. It's up to you to make up information in the story, such as who the main characters are, where the story takes place, and what happens.

▶ **TIP 1: Describe your characters.**

Readers want to know what characters look like, how they walk, what they wear, how they feel about things, and even what their personal habits are. The more the author tells about a character, the more real the story becomes for the readers.

What are some details you like to know about characters in stories you read?

_____

_____

If a story has more than one main character, make them different enough so that your readers can tell them apart by their actions as well as their words.

TIP 2: Develop a clear setting for the action.

Tell your readers where the action takes place (a canoe, a park, a farm, the 27th floor of a skyscraper) and when it takes place (now, a hundred years ago, or a thousand years in the future).

What other details might you include in the setting of a story?

_____

_____

 TIP 3: Use dialogue (conversation between characters).

When characters do their own talking, they develop their own personalities and give a sense of realism to the story. Dialogue also allows the writer to present information in a variety of ways.

On the following lines, write a short conversation that you had today. (Be sure to use quotation marks and commas.)

 TIP 4: Give physical details through your characters' senses.

As the action progresses, let the reader know what the characters see, hear, and feel. In some stories, you may even want to describe what your characters taste or smell.

TIP 5: Create a main conflict to develop the plot (events and actions).

In most stories, the main characters must overcome some kind of problem. If you can keep your character working to solve the main problem, your readers will stay interested. Maybe your character is lost in a dark jungle, trying to join a neighborhood club, or building a secret hideaway in the woods. Just make sure that the character has troubles with whatever he or she is doing. These problems will develop your plot. Have your characters working to resolve the main problem, which will lead to an ending for your story. Remember to show the action happening using vivid details; don't just tell your readers about it.

What are some kinds of story conflicts that interest you?

_____

_____

TIP 6: Decide who will tell the story.

When you write a story, you need to decide who the storyteller will be. From whose point of view will the story be told? Will it be the main character, who can only describe what he or she thinks, feels, hears, and sees? Or will it be an all-knowing storyteller who can describe the actions, feelings, and thoughts of all the characters? It's up to you to decide—just make sure you stick with the same storyteller's point of view throughout the whole story.

Topic 1: Fictional Narrative

Have you ever planned to do something and then had everything go wrong? Maybe you and your family planned a picnic, and it rained the entire day. Maybe you took a trip, and the driver got lost. Maybe you borrowed a friend's bike, crashed it, and had to run errands for a month to make enough money to repair it. These things may not have been fun (or funny) at the time, but later you probably enjoyed telling people how you dealt with your problems. Problems make good stories. Readers enjoy stories that tell how characters overcome their troubles.

Prewriting Activity

Directions: In this exercise, you will plan and write a fictional narrative (made-up story). Your story will tell what happens to a character when he or she is taking care of the neighbor's pet monkey and it runs away.

Your story can be realistic (something that could easily happen), or it can be a wild, almost unbelievable tale. You are writing the story; anything can happen to your characters if you say it happens!

The following questions will help you plan your story. Write your ideas in the spaces provided.

1. **Tell about the main character.**

   What is the main character's name? _____

   Describe the main character. _____

   _____

   _____

   _____

What is the monkey's name? _____

Describe the monkey. _____

_____

_____

_____

2. **Tell about the setting.**

    A. Where does the story take place? What neighborhood, country, planet, and so on?

        _____

        _____

        Does the story take place indoors or outdoors?

        _____

        Does the setting have any important buildings or geographical features?

        _____

        _____

        Does the setting have any important furniture, equipment, and so on?

        _____

        _____

B. When does the story take place?

Past, present, or future? _____

Time of year? _____

Time of day? _____

Weather? _____

3. **Tell about the plot.**

How do the main character's problems start?

_____

What other problems does the main character run into?

_____

_____

What happens to get the main character out of trouble?

_____

_____

How does your story end?

_____

_____

4. **Decide who will tell the story.**

From whose point of view will your story be told?

_____

Writing Assignment

Directions: Now you will write a fictional (made-up) narrative based on the ideas you came up with for the "lost monkey" story. Your story should explain who the characters are, where the action takes place, how the monkey gets away from the main character, and what the main character does to get the monkey back. Use the ideas that you developed in the Prewriting Activity.

Look at the checklist on this page. It tells what your fictional narrative should include. Use it to revise and edit your work. Check each box as you complete the task.

Use a pencil to write your narrative. You may erase, cross out, or make changes in your work, but keep your paper as neat as possible.

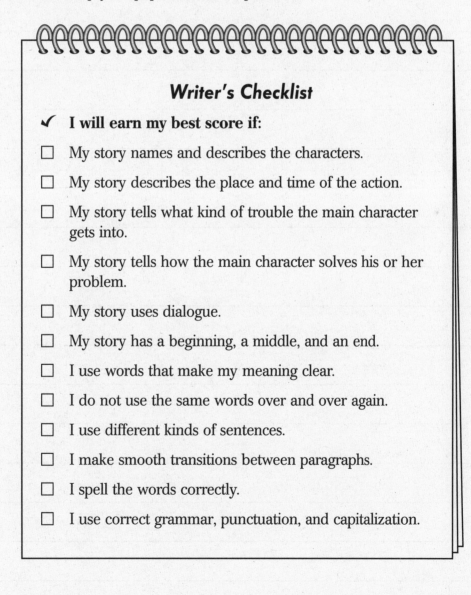

Writer's Checklist

✔ **I will earn my best score if:**

☐ My story names and describes the characters.

☐ My story describes the place and time of the action.

☐ My story tells what kind of trouble the main character gets into.

☐ My story tells how the main character solves his or her problem.

☐ My story uses dialogue.

☐ My story has a beginning, a middle, and an end.

☐ I use words that make my meaning clear.

☐ I do not use the same words over and over again.

☐ I use different kinds of sentences.

☐ I make smooth transitions between paragraphs.

☐ I spell the words correctly.

☐ I use correct grammar, punctuation, and capitalization.

Directions: Write your story on the following lines.

_____

_____

_____

_____

_____

_____

_____

_____

_____

_____

_____

_____

_____

_____

_____

_____

_____

_____

_____

_____

_____

_____

_____

_____

_____

_____

_____

_____

_____

_____

_____

_____

_____

_____

_____

_____

_____

_____

_____

Lesson 20: Personal Experience Narratives

Look at the book titles above. Which personal experience narrative would you probably skip? You may not have had a life-threatening experience or had your grandfather as a student, but you have no doubt experienced new and exciting things—you shouldn't have to write about your shoelaces to create a personal narrative.

A **personal experience narrative** is a story about something in your own life. It might be about a place you visited, an experience at school, something you and a friend did together, or anything else that has happened to or around you. The possibilities are endless. Your experiences with neighbors, friends, relatives, sports, trips, fears, successes—any of these might make an interesting topic to write about.

Personal experience narratives give you a chance to show your feelings and your personality. You can be serious or you can be humorous. You can discuss things that make you happy, angry, hopeful, or sad. It's a story about you and what you've seen, so write it from your own point of view.

▷ **TIP 1: Plan a beginning, a middle, and an end.**

As with most other kinds of writing, a personal narrative should be organized. The narrative should have an introduction, a body, and a conclusion. Keeping this in mind will help you choose the story's most important events and details and put them in a reasonable order.

TIP 2: Pick an experience that excites you.

Most topics assigned in the classroom or on a test will be fairly broad. As you do your brainstorming or freewriting, narrow down the subject to a very specific experience that excites your imagination. If you are excited about your subject, you will write a more interesting narrative.

 TIP 3: Remember how things looked, sounded, smelled, felt, and tasted.

Use physical details to bring your reader into the action of the story. Describe the happenings just as you did in the fictional narrative.

 TIP 4: Use dialogue (conversation between characters).

Even if you don't remember conversations exactly, use dialogue that is as close as you can recall. Remember, dialogue helps readers learn about your characters. It also makes the narrative more interesting and more "real" to the reader.

 TIP 5: Be honest.

Don't worry about making yourself "look good." Readers will like your narrative much more if you are honest about your mistakes, shortcomings, and fears. Let your readers know how you felt about the events that happened. For example, if you were really frightened the first time you went to school, tell your reader about it. It will make your narrative more interesting and fun to read.

 TIP 6: Have a main conflict (problem).

Keep the main conflict (the main character's biggest problem) in mind as you write. Most good stories have a conflict that centers on the main character. This character must overcome some problem to get what he or she wants or needs. If you tell about problems in your personal experience narrative, you will keep your reader's interest.

On the lines below, write a few ideas for personal experience narratives you might like to share with your readers.

_____

_____

_____

_____

Topic 2: Personal Experience Narrative

Prewriting Activity

Directions: In this exercise, you will write a personal experience narrative that describes a new experience that you were excited to try for the first time. (Some examples might include going to camp, batting for the first time in a baseball game, or riding a skateboard.) To help you come up with some ideas, complete the following activities.

1. On the following lines, list three or more examples of new things that you were excited to try.

   _____

   _____

   _____

   _____

2. Look over your list. Circle the experience that you would like to write about.

3. When did this experience happen?

   _____

4. Where did this experience happen?

   _____

5. Were there other people involved? Who?

   _____

   _____

   _____

6. How did you feel before the experience? Circle any of the words below that apply:

thrilled   eager   inspired

anxious   hyper

Add a word or two of your own. _____

7. How did you feel during the experience? Circle any of the words below that apply:

calm   frightened   shaky

fearless   confident

Add a word or two of your own. _____

8. How did you feel after the experience? Circle any of the words below that apply:

happy   relieved   tired

joyful   proud

Add a word or two of your own. _____

9. What are some details you remember about the way things looked, sounded, and felt to you before the experience?

_____

_____

During the experience?

_____

_____

After the experience?

_____

_____

10. What did you learn about yourself because of this experience?

_____

_____

_____

_____

_____

_____

_____

Writing Assignment

Directions: In this exercise, you will use the Prewriting Activity you just completed to write a personal experience narrative. Write about an experience that you were excited to try for the first time.

Be sure your story has a beginning, a middle, and an end. Use words that make your meaning clear—and be honest.

Look at the checklist on the next page. It tells what your personal experience narrative should include. Use it to revise and edit your work. Check each box as you complete the task.

Use a pencil to write your narrative. You may erase, cross out, or make changes in your work, but keep your paper as neat as possible.

Writer's Checklist

✓ **I will earn my best score if:**

☐ My narrative tells how I handled my excitement about doing something new for the first time.

☐ My narrative has a beginning, a middle, and an end.

☐ My narrative uses specific details to describe people, places, things, and feelings.

☐ My narrative uses dialogue to tell what the characters said.

☐ My narrative tells about happenings before, during, and after my experience.

☐ I use words that make my meaning clear.

☐ I do not use the same words over and over.

☐ I use different kinds of sentences.

☐ I make smooth transitions between paragraphs.

☐ I spell the words correctly.

☐ I use correct grammar, punctuation, and capitalization.

Directions: Write your narrative on the following lines.

_____

_____

_____

_____

_____

_____

_____

_____

_____

_____

_____

_____

_____

_____

_____

_____

_____

_____

_____

_____

_____

_____

_____

_____

_____

_____

_____

_____

_____

_____

_____

_____

_____

_____

_____

_____

_____

_____

_____

Lesson 21: Responding to Literature

"That was the best book I've ever read."

"I *hate* poems about kissing!"

"That short story wasn't nearly short enough."

When you are talking to your friends about a novel, a short story, a poem, or a play, you might say something similar to one of these statements. And that's okay when you are talking to your friends. But when you write a response to literature (write about something you have read), you need to say more. You need to support what you write with examples from the text. The following tips will help you when you write a response to a piece of literature.

> **TIP 1: Read a piece of literature carefully before responding to it.**

It's hard to write a response to something you don't know anything about. You need to read the piece of literature carefully to understand its main idea and the message the author is trying to get across. Then you will be able to respond thoughtfully.

> **TIP 2: Don't just summarize what you've read.**

When you respond to a piece of literature, you need to do more than just write a summary of what you've read. Write about what you think the meaning of the work is and why you think so.

> **TIP 3: Think about how a piece of literature makes you feel.**

Not everyone feels the same way about every piece of literature. Something that you think is really funny might seem silly to someone else. Neither opinion is wrong. The important thing is to explain why the writing makes you feel the way it does.

> **TIP 4: Use examples from a piece of literature to support your ideas.**

Get specific to make your point. Instead of telling that the middle part of a story is sad, tell how sad Chapter 3 is when Stan loses the city chess championship to the girl from Ipanema Elementary School. The more examples you use from the actual writing, the better your audience will understand what you are saying about the writing. If you use actual sentences or phrases from the story, be sure to put them in quotes.

TIP 5: Organize your response.

Just like any other kind of writing, your response should include an introduction, a body, and a conclusion. The main idea of your response should be the most important thing you want to say about the piece of literature, and you should support the main idea in your body and conclusion.

Topic 3: Literary Response

Directions: Read the following poem.

The Butterbean Tent

by Elizabeth Madox Roberts

All through the garden I went and went,
And I walked in under the butterbean tent.

The poles leaned up like a good tepee
And made a nice little house for me.

I had a hard brown clod for a seat,
And all outside was a cool green street.

A little green worm and a butterfly
And a cricket-like thing that could hop went by.

Hidden away there were flocks and flocks
Of bugs that could go like little clocks.

Such a good day it was when I spent
A long, long while in the butterbean tent.

Prewriting Activity

Directions: You will write an essay responding to the poem "The Butterbean Tent" by Elizabeth Madox Roberts. Choose one of the following topics.

1. How do you think the author feels about spending time in the garden?

2. What are your thoughts about the poem? How does the poem make you feel? Why?

3. Respond to the poem in your own way.

Before you begin to write, brainstorm or freewrite your thoughts about the poem and create an outline for your response in the space that follows.

Writing Assignment

Directions: Write a response to the poem "The Butterbean Tent" using your prewriting ideas from page 128.

Use the following checklist to make sure your writing is the best it can be.

Writer's Checklist

✓ **I will earn my best score if:**

☐ My response clearly states my main idea.

☐ My response contains specific references from the text that support my thoughts about the poem.

☐ My response is well organized and complete.

☐ My response is written in an interesting way, using a variety of sentences.

☐ I use words that make my meaning clear.

☐ I spell the words correctly.

☐ I use correct grammar, punctuation, and capitalization.

Directions: Write your response on the following lines.

_____

_____

_____

_____

_____

_____

_____

_____

_____

_____

_____

_____

_____

_____

_____

_____

_____

_____

_____

_____

_____

_____

_____

_____

_____

_____

_____

_____

_____

_____

_____

_____

_____

_____

_____

_____

_____

_____

_____

_____

_____

Lesson 22: Informational Writing

When you do **informational writing**, you explain something to your readers. The goal in this type of writing is to present your information as clearly as possible. By sharing your topic in a way that makes it easy for readers to understand, you are like a teacher giving information to students.

A report is one kind of informational writing. To write a report, you'll need an interesting topic, some good information about your topic, and a way to organize your research and writing. Here are a few tips for writing informational essays and reports.

TIP 1: Select a topic.

If you are selecting your own topic, use the brainstorming and freewriting methods discussed in Unit 1 until you find a subject you would like to write about.

TIP 2: Gather the information.

An encyclopedia is usually a good place to begin. It will not only give you general information about almost any subject, but will also give you a list of additional sources on many topics.

There are many other places to find what you need:

- **Visit the library.** The staff can help you find books, newspaper articles, and magazines that address your subject.

- **Ask the librarian about CD-ROMs.** Many encyclopedias and other reference materials are now available in this easy-to-use format.

- **Get on the Internet.** An entire world of websites is waiting to give you information on just about any topic you can imagine.

- **Interview a local expert.** First, select a person who works in the field about which you intend to write. Then politely request a brief (10 or 15 minutes) appointment. Many busy people will make time to help a serious—and courteous—student. Think carefully about which questions you will ask, and see if you can look up the answers to them first. Keep only the questions that use the expert's special knowledge.

Make sure the information you find is current and accurate. Is your source a book written by an expert, or is it a paper on the Internet written by a student? It's best to use many sources, but the information contained in each should be based on good research.

TIP 3: Organize the information.

Start by trying to see the overall picture. How does all your information fit together? Once you've decided that, arrange your information in the way that best fits your topic.

Information for reports can be organized in several ways. Choose the one that makes the most sense for the topic you've chosen:

- by date or order of events (first to last)
- by major ideas (major idea 1, major idea 2, and so on)
- by order of importance (from most important to least important, or from least important to most important)
- by different sides of an issue (for, against, undecided)
- by comparing two or more ideas
- by explaining how or why something happens using causes and effects

TIP 4: Write down the main idea.

When you start a report by putting your main idea into a single sentence, you begin to develop a clear purpose for your paper. Keeping the main idea in mind will help you come up with good supporting ideas. It will also help you focus your research on the important things needed to develop your topic.

TIP 5: Write down some supporting ideas.

After you have written your main idea, find some ideas to support it. Put each supporting idea into one sentence. These should be general statements.

TIP 6: List facts and examples about each supporting idea.

After you have written all your supporting ideas, go back and list the important facts and examples that support each idea.

TIP 7: Connect facts to supporting ideas with clear sentences.

Give each supporting idea at least one paragraph. Write clear, focused sentences using the facts to strengthen your supporting ideas. Use transitional words and phrases to connect all your ideas.

TIP 8: Sum up the information.

Write a concluding paragraph that summarizes what you have written. If possible, show how your summary ties in with your opening sentence or paragraph.

TIP 9: Tell where you found your information.

If you use anyone else's exact words, put quotation marks around those words and tell who wrote or said them. You should also make a bibliography (a list of books, magazines, and so on) at the end of your essay telling where you found the information you have used in your report. Each entry in your bibliography should have the title and author of the book or article. You may also include the publisher and the date when the book or article was published, along with the page numbers where the information was found. Here are two examples:

An article in a magazine

> Rosing, Norbert. "Polar Bears." *National Geographic,* December 2000, pp. 30–39.

A book

> Sachar, Louis. *Sideways Stories from Wayside School.* Scott Foresman, 1993.

Don't forget the basics of all good writing:

- Use complete sentences.
- Use correct grammar, punctuation, capitalization, and spelling.
- Vary the length and wording of your sentences.
- Make smooth transitions between paragraphs.
- Use only the information that covers your topic. Don't give your readers extra details that aren't strongly connected to your main idea and supporting ideas.

In the space below, list some topics you would find interesting enough to write a report about.

_____

_____

_____

_____

Topic 4: Informational Writing

Directions: Imagine that you have been asked to write a report about puppets. During your research, you find information about puppets in three sources: an encyclopedia, a magazine, and a book. Read the information from these sources provided below and on the next two pages. You will use this information to complete the Prewriting Activity on pages 137 and 138, and the Writing Assignment on pages 139 through 141.

From an encyclopedia:

Puppet A puppet is an artificial person, animal, or thing that is controlled by a human. Puppets can be moved by strings, rods, wires, or by direct movement of the fingers, hands, and arms. The puppet's voice is supplied by the puppeteer—the person directing its movement. There are many kinds of puppets: hand puppets, string puppets, rod puppets, shadow puppets, and ventriloquists' dummies. The most common types of puppets in the United States are the hand puppet and the string puppet, or marionette. A hand puppet is controlled by the puppeteer's hand, which fits inside the puppet's head. A marionette is controlled by strings or wires attached to the puppet's body parts.

Some teachers use puppets to make learning more interesting and enjoyable. For example, puppets are used to act out famous events in history. They are also used to teach citizenship, health care, and other subjects. In addition, puppets have been used successfully in teaching foreign languages to children. And, by creating voices for puppets, some children have overcome serious speech problems.

Puppets have provided entertainment for thousands of years. Archaeologists have found puppets in ancient Egyptian and Roman tombs. Researchers believe that the first puppets were most likely used in religious and cultural ceremonies. They have strong evidence that marionettes were popular during the Middle Ages (from about a.d. 500 to 1500). Children often enjoy making their own puppets from common household items such as socks, paper bags, milk cartons, and pieces of wood. Some children write and perform puppet shows, changing their voices for the different puppet characters.

From a magazine:

Hand puppets are the most common kind of puppet used in the United States today. They are called hand puppets because they fit directly over, and are controlled by, the puppeteer's hand. Regular hand puppets consist of a hollow head and a sleeve that serves as part of the puppet's body. The puppeteer places one arm through the puppet's "body" sleeve. The puppeteer's thumb fits into one of the puppet's arms and the pinkie fits into the puppet's other arm. The puppeteer's index and middle fingers are placed inside the head. Hand puppets usually have neither legs nor feet.

Larger hand puppets have become popular since American puppeteer Jim Henson developed the Muppets for television. Muppets are usually made of foam rubber. They have very wide mouths. The puppeteer's thumb fits into the lower jaw and the fingers form the upper part of the Muppet's face. The operator can move his or her fingers to change both the Muppet's expression and the shape of its head.

From a book:

Marionettes, sometimes called string puppets, have complete, jointed bodies. Each body part (head, torso, arms, hands, knees, and feet) is attached to a string, thread, or wire. A puppeteer sitting above the stage holds onto a control device to which all of the strings are connected. The puppeteer moves the marionette's body parts by manipulating the control device. Marionettes are considered to be the most difficult type of puppet to master. Some are so complicated that they can imitate almost every human or animal action.

The word *marionette* is French for *Little Mary,* the name of a string-puppet character popular during the Middle Ages. Marionettes were not fully developed until around 1850, although they have existed in some form for centuries. A few ancient examples of this type of puppet have been found in Europe.

Prewriting Activity

Directions: Using the information you have read, write a short report about puppets. You don't have to use all of the information. Use only the facts that will help support your main idea. On the lines provided, fill in the information that you will use to write your report.

Notice that the information you have been provided gives the greatest detail in three areas:

- the history of puppets

- details about hand puppets

- details about string puppets (marionettes)

What is the main idea you want to write about in your report? (The sentence you write to answer this question should work as your topic sentence.)

_____

_____

_____

Go back to the passages and underline the supporting ideas that you want to use. Then write them in your own words on the lines below. Use at least three supporting ideas.

1. _____

   _____

2. _____

   _____

3. _____

   _____

What facts or examples support each of the supporting ideas you listed on page 137? Circle them in the passages. Then write them in your own words on the lines below.

Fact/Example 1: _____

_____

_____

Fact/Example 2: _____

_____

_____

Fact/Example 3: _____

_____

_____

Write a concluding statement to sum up your ideas. (Make this statement tie back to your opening sentence or paragraph.)

_____

_____

_____

_____

Writing Assignment

Directions: In this exercise, you will write a report about puppets. In the report, you will write a topic sentence that states your main idea. You will also include two or three major supporting ideas, with facts to back them up. Conclude your report by summarizing what you have written. Tie your conclusion back to the topic sentence if you can.

Use the information you organized in the Prewriting Activity and be sure to use words that make your meaning clear. Also, make sure your report is well organized and complete.

Look at the checklist below. It tells what your report should include. Use it to revise and edit your writing. Check each box when you have completed the task.

Use a pencil to write your report. You may erase, cross out, or make changes in your work, but keep your paper as neat as possible.

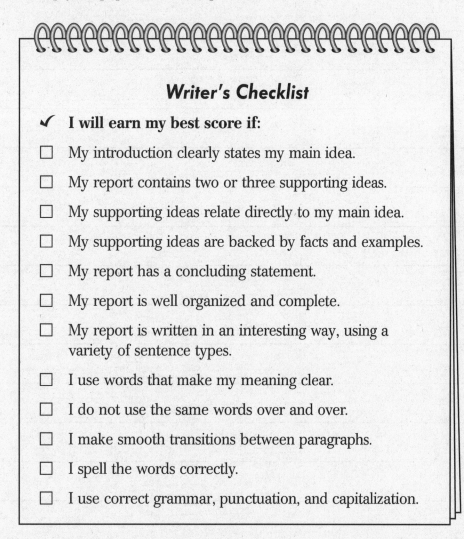

Writer's Checklist

✔ **I will earn my best score if:**

☐ My introduction clearly states my main idea.

☐ My report contains two or three supporting ideas.

☐ My supporting ideas relate directly to my main idea.

☐ My supporting ideas are backed by facts and examples.

☐ My report has a concluding statement.

☐ My report is well organized and complete.

☐ My report is written in an interesting way, using a variety of sentence types.

☐ I use words that make my meaning clear.

☐ I do not use the same words over and over.

☐ I make smooth transitions between paragraphs.

☐ I spell the words correctly.

☐ I use correct grammar, punctuation, and capitalization.

Directions: Write your report on the following lines.

_____

_____

_____

_____

_____

_____

_____

_____

_____

_____

_____

_____

_____

_____

_____

_____

_____

_____

_____

_____

_____

_____

_____

_____

_____

_____

_____

_____

_____

_____

_____

_____

_____

_____

_____

_____

_____

_____

_____

Lesson 23: Writing a Summary

Sometimes writing tests will ask you to summarize a reading passage. This probably sounds harder than it really is. Unless you're the kind of person who has to tell everyone you meet every single detail of your life, you summarize all the time.

You summarize when you tell a friend what happened on your favorite TV show last night. You summarize when you tell your mom or dad what you learned in school. And you probably summarize when you tell your friends about something you did last weekend.

TIP 1: Skim the title and the selection to find out what it's mostly about.

TIP 2: Read the selection carefully, looking for key (important) words and phrases.

TIP 3: Write down the main idea of the selection using your own words.

This sentence will usually become your topic sentence.

TIP 4: Now write a main idea sentence for each paragraph.

Later, you may wish to combine the main ideas of two or more paragraphs.

TIP 5: Add important details that support your main ideas.

TIP 6: Arrange the sentences in a logical order, based on the content of the original selection.

TIP 7: Restate the main idea in a concluding sentence.

TIP 8: Put everything in your own words.

Do NOT copy sentences from the selection.

TIP 9: In general, shorter is better.

A good rule of thumb is to make a summary no more than one-third as long as the original selection.

Topic 5: Writing a Summary

Directions: Read the selection below. You will summarize it for the next exercise.

Sequoyah and the "Talking Leaves"

by Loric Koziol

1   Sequoyah was born about 1770 in the peaceful Cherokee village of Tuskegee, Tennessee. He grew up in the Smoky Mountains of eastern Tennessee. Reared in the ways of the Cherokee, the boy learned the tribal customs. He became a capable hunter and fur trader, but he had other talents, too. He could draw, make silver jewelry, and build wood furniture. He also was a respected blacksmith.

2   When Sequoyah was a young man, he saw English-speaking people reading and writing books and letters. He was fascinated by their ability to communicate with marks made upon pages of paper. He called such pages "talking leaves." The Cherokee, Sequoyah knew, had no such written language.

3   About 1809, many Cherokee people began moving west to escape white settlers. Sequoyah was concerned that his people would be split apart without any means of communication. He believed that a written Cherokee language could help the tribe communicate with each other from scattered locations. The young man set his mind to work on the problem. He didn't know it, but he was beginning a 12-year struggle to put the Cherokee language into a written form and to get it accepted by tribal leaders.

4   During many long years of work, Sequoyah created a syllabary, a set of characters that represent sounds. (The characters in a syllabary are similar to an alphabet, except that each drawing represents a syllable, not an individual letter.) Sequoyah broke the Cherokee language into 85 different sounds, or syllables, and then drew a symbol, or character, to represent each sound. His young daughter, Ahyoka, easily learned the system. Before long, she could communicate with her father using his written symbols.

5   Finally, Sequoyah and Ahyoka got the chance to demonstrate to tribal elders the usefulness of his system. The elders were unsure as Sequoyah read the words they had privately told Ahyoka to write. When it was her turn, Ahyoka read words the elders had told Sequoyah to write. The elders were at last convinced.

6   Praise for Sequoyah's "invention" spread rapidly. In 1821, his syllabary was adopted by the Cherokee nation. Within months, thousands of Cherokees had learned to read and write their own language. Then, in 1828, the first Cherokee-language newspaper was published. The lives of the Cherokee people would be changed forever by Sequoyah's syllabary.

Prewriting Activity

Directions: Write a summary of the article about Sequoyah. Start by finding the main idea of the selection. Then find the main idea of each paragraph. Using your own words, fill in the main ideas on the lines below.

What is the main idea of the selection?

_____

_____

_____

_____

What is the main idea of paragraph 1?

_____

_____

_____

What is the main idea of paragraph 2?

_____

_____

_____

What is the main idea of paragraph 3?

_____

_____

_____

What is the main idea of paragraph 4?

_____

_____

_____

What is the main idea of paragraph 5?

_____

_____

_____

What is the main idea of paragraph 6?

_____

_____

_____

List any important details that support the main ideas.

_____

_____

_____

_____

Write a concluding statement that restates the main idea.

_____

_____

_____

_____

Writing Assignment

Directions: Use the information that you have gathered in your Prewriting Activity to summarize the selection about Sequoyah. In your summary, you will tell the most important points from the selection in one paragraph.

Be sure to use words that make your meaning clear, and don't use the exact words that the author of the selection used.

Use the checklist on this page to make sure your writing is the best it can be.

Writer's Checklist

✓ **I will earn my best score if:**

☐ My summary is written in my own words.

☐ My summary is about one-third as long as the original selection.

☐ My summary begins with a topic sentence that tells the main idea of the original selection.

☐ My summary includes all of the main ideas of the selection.

☐ My summary includes all important supporting details (but no unimportant information).

☐ My summary ends with a concluding sentence.

☐ My summary is well organized and complete.

☐ I use words that make my meaning clear.

☐ I do not use the same words over and over again.

☐ I spell the words correctly.

☐ I use correct grammar, punctuation, and capitalization.

Directions: Write your summary on the lines that follow.

_____

_____

_____

_____

_____

_____

_____

_____

_____

_____

_____

_____

_____

_____

_____

_____

_____

_____

Lesson 24: Business Letters

Tony Hawk, Skateboarder
X-Gamer

Dear Mr. Hawk:

Hi, how are you? I am fine. I hope you are fine, too.
I saw your face in one a them milk ads. I got a
question for you? I don't really like milk, but I would
like to be in a ad if I could have my pixure in a majer
magazeen (and make some big bucks, too!). Here
are some pixures of me with a milk musstash.
Could you help me get a jobb?
Thanx for you're help. I am you're biggest fan. I really
like the way you handel your bicycle.

Sinseerly,

Jason Callawander

If you were to write a letter like Jason Callawander's, what kind of reaction do you think you would get? In this lesson, you will learn the proper way to write a formal letter.

TIP 1: Be direct.

Most people who receive business mail must read several letters a day. A polite letter that gets right to the point saves them time and is most likely to get prompt, professional attention. Say what you need to say, but no more. This isn't the place to try to strike up a friendship or impress your reader with your creative-writing skills.

 TIP 2: Be polite.

Most likely, you've never met the people who'll receive your business letters. They're neither your friends nor your relatives. Write to them as you would speak to your teacher, your principal, or even the president. Never use slang or casual, everyday language. Keep the tone of your letter as businesslike as you can.

 TIP 3: Be neat and use correct spelling and grammar.

A messy letter tells your reader that you don't think enough of him or her to be careful. Such a letter may well end up in the trash.

TIP 4: Make sure your information is correct.

If you are going to write to a football player, don't tell him you like how he plays basketball.

TIP 5: Use a business letter format.

Two possible formats are shown on the following page. You should use one of these whenever you write a business letter.

Now take another look at Jason's letter. How well did he follow the guidelines above?

Pick Your Style

Formal letters are written in **full-block letter format** or **modified-block letter format**. Look at the two examples below:

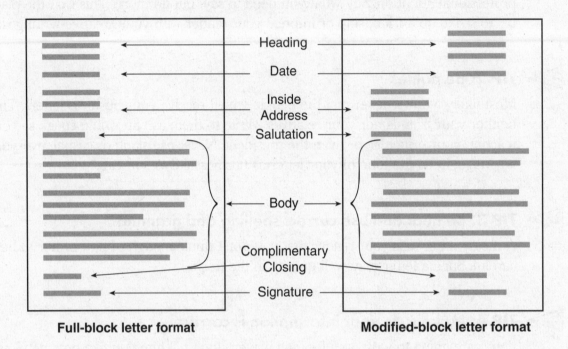

Full-block letter format   **Modified-block letter format**

A business letter uses a format similar to that of an informal letter, such as one you would write to a good friend. You should also include a **heading** and an **inside address**. The heading includes your name and address. The inside address is placed after the date, just above the salutation (greeting). It includes the name and address of the person to whom the letter is addressed. This information usually fits on three or four lines.

Topic 6: Business Letter

Directions: Imagine that while on vacation with your family you stopped at a little diner called Phil's Place. The grilled cheese was okay, but the apple pie was amazing. It was so good that you think about it during the day and dream about it at night. You learned that the owner is Phil Carson and the address is: 123 Main St., Eugene, OR 97401.

✏️ Prewriting Activity

Directions: You decide to write a business letter asking Phil for his apple pie recipe. Underline any important information on page 152 that you want to be sure to mention in your letter.

What is your name and address? (Heading)

Name: _____

Street address: _____

City, state, and ZIP code:_____

To whom are you sending this letter? (Inside Address)

Name: _____

Street address: _____

City, state, and ZIP code:_____

(**Note:** Remember, don't use a comma between state and ZIP code in the above addresses or on the envelope.)

What is today's date?_____

What salutation (greeting) will you use? _____

_____

What will the body of your letter say?

Who are you?_____

Why did you visit Phil's Place?_____

_____

What is the purpose of your letter? _____

_____

_____

What will you say to thank the reader for his or her time?

_____

_____

_____

What will you use as your complimentary closing?

_____

(Remember to sign your letter following the complimentary closing.)

Writing Assignment

Directions: In this exercise, you will write a formal business letter to Phil Carson asking for his apple pie recipe. You will tell him who you are (a student? a pie lover?), when it was that you visited Phil's place, and why you are writing.

Use the information that you wrote in the Prewriting Activity to organize and develop your letter. Remember: Be polite, be direct, and be brief.

Use the checklist on this page to make sure your writing is the best it can be.

Writer's Checklist

✓ **I will earn my best score if:**

☐ My letter has a heading and inside address.

☐ My letter uses a full-block or modified-block business letter format.

☐ My letter tells what I want the company to do.

☐ My letter is polite, direct, and brief.

☐ My letter is well organized and complete.

☐ My letter is neat.

☐ I use words that make my meaning clear.

☐ I do not use the same words over and over.

☐ I make smooth transitions between paragraphs.

☐ I spell the words correctly.

☐ I use correct grammar, punctuation, and capitalization.

Directions: Write your letter on the following lines.

_____

_____

_____

_____

_____

_____

_____

_____

_____

_____

_____

_____

_____

_____

Lesson 25: Letters to the Editor

Dear Editor:

Thanks to the quick thinking of a young Reno student, I am alive today. Last week, on my way to Carson City, I stopped at Joe's Diner for a sandwich. While eating, I choked on my food. A local elementary school student saw me struggling to breathe and rushed to my aid. Fifth-grader Michelle Goodenough grabbed me from behind and did the Heimlich maneuver. Suddenly, I was able to breathe again. Michelle said she had learned this lifesaving move in health class at King Elementary School.

After this experience, I plan to urge school officials to include lifesaving instruction as a part of our school system's health classes. I hope your readers will join me in my efforts to make this kind of learning available to all students.

Thank you, Michelle, for saving my life. And thank you, too, King Elementary School, for training your students to handle emergencies.

Raphael Cramden,
Hawthorne, Nevada

A letter to the editor states an opinion and sometimes tries to persuade. If your letter is interesting and well written, there's a good chance the editor will print it in his or her publication.

> **TIP 1: There are many reasons for writing a letter to the editor.**

Here are some of those reasons:

- commenting on a government policy
- raising an issue that is of interest to other readers
- publicly thanking a person, group, or organization
- suggesting ways to improve the community
- congratulating people, groups, or organizations
- seeking support for projects or activities

As you can see, letters to the editor can be about almost any subject that might be of interest to the publication's readers.

TIP 2: Letters to the editor should be written as formal business letters.

Remember the following:

- Be direct.
- Be brief.
- Be polite.
- Be neat.
- Use correct spelling and grammar.
- Use a business letter format.

Topic 7: Letter to the Editor

Because of overcrowding at the city library, officials have established a new rule. They have decided to limit the number of hours that persons under the age of 18 can use the library. Until recently, the city library was open to everyone from 8 A.M. until 9 P.M. Now, people under 18 must be out of the library by 4 P.M. on weekdays and 2 P.M. on Saturdays and Sundays. These hours apply even if people under 18 are accompanied by an adult.

All persons 18 and older will be allowed to use the library until the normal closing time.

Prewriting Activity

Directions: You have decided to write a letter to the editor of your local newspaper. You want to explain why this new rule is unfair to students on summer vacation. Also, you want to ask readers to support your ideas. You will ask them to write their city council members asking that the new rule be changed.

Use the spaces below to organize a persuasive letter to the editor.

Your name and address: (Heading)

Your name: _____

Your street address: _____

Your city, state, and ZIP code: _____

To whom are you writing? (Inside Address)

Editor's name: _____

Name of newspaper: _____

Street address: _____

City, state, and ZIP code:_____

What is the date? _____

What salutation (greeting) will you use?

_____

Write one sentence telling how you feel about the city's new library hours.

_____

_____

_____

List three reasons why you believe the new rule is unfair to persons under the age of 18.

_____

_____

_____

_____

_____

_____

What do you think city officials should do?

_____

_____

_____

What do you want readers to do?

_____

_____

_____

What will you use as your complimentary closing?

_____

(Remember to sign your letter following the complimentary closing.)

Writing Assignment

Directions: In this exercise you will write a letter to the editor. In your letter, you will explain why the library's new hours are unfair to students on summer vacation. Also, you will ask readers to support you by writing to their city council members, urging them to change the new rule.

Use the information that you wrote in the Prewriting Activity to organize and develop your letter. Remember: Be polite, be direct, and be brief.

Use the checklist on this page to make sure your writing is the best it can be.

Writer's Checklist

✔ **I will earn my best score if:**

☐ My letter has a heading and inside address.

☐ My letter uses a full-block or modified-block business letter format.

☐ My letter tells how I feel about the new library hours.

☐ My letter tells why I disagree with the new policy by giving supporting information.

☐ My letter tells what I want readers to do.

☐ My letter tells what I want city officials to do.

☐ My letter is polite, direct, and brief.

☐ My letter is well organized and complete.

☐ My letter is neat.

☐ I use words that make my meaning clear.

☐ I do not use the same words over and over.

☐ I spell the words correctly.

☐ I use correct grammar, punctuation, and capitalization.

Directions: Write your letter on the following lines.

_____

_____

_____

_____

_____

_____

_____

_____

_____

_____

_____

_____

_____

_____

_____

_____

Standards and Skills: 1.2, 3.4

Lesson 26: Persuasive Writing

When Kenny and Max want to go to space camp, their parents tell them to put their reasons in writing. "Convince us," they say. Here's Kenny's note to his parents:

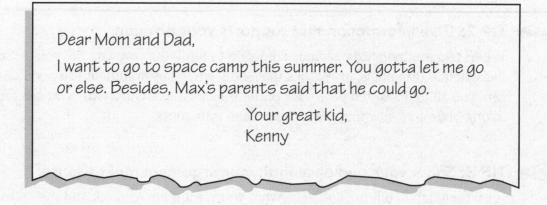

Dear Mom and Dad,

I want to go to space camp this summer. You gotta let me go or else. Besides, Max's parents said that he could go.

Your great kid,
Kenny

What does Kenny want his parents to do?

_____

_____

What facts does Kenny use to support his position?

_____

_____

How effective do you think this note will be? It doesn't give Kenny's parents any real reasons to support his request to go to space camp. It looks as if Kenny could use some help persuading them.

When you try to persuade someone to agree with your viewpoint, you try to talk them into thinking or doing something in a certain way—*your* way! Persuasive writing does the same thing. To be effective, persuasive writing must include facts to support your position, and it must explain how those facts are important.

If Kenny had read the following tips, his "persuasive" letter might have been a little more persuasive.

TIP 1: State your position clearly.

When you are trying to persuade someone to agree with your ideas, the first thing you must do is be clear about what your ideas are. Tell your audience what you want them to think or believe.

TIP 2: Give information that supports your position.

When you are trying to persuade someone to think the way you do, you must include facts, details, examples, or reasons that show why your argument is a good one. If you can, you should also tell how your position helps them. Otherwise, you are simply asking your audience to replace their ideas with yours.

TIP 3: Show your audience that your argument makes sense.

It isn't enough to tell the audience what you want them to think and then write down a bunch of facts. In order for your writing to be persuasive, you must show your audience *how* the facts support your argument.

One way to do this is to first explain your argument, then explain an opposing argument, and finally show how your argument is the better one.

TIP 4: Tell your audience what action you want them to take.

You have presented your argument and shown why it is a good one. Now is the time to tell your audience what you want them to do. You might want your teacher to give you less homework. Or maybe you will tell your parents that they should let you go to space camp. Whatever action you tell your audience to take, make sure you have shown them why it is the right action to take.

TIP 5: Persuasive writing can be in the form of a letter or an essay.

Kenny chose to make his arguments in a letter to his parents. He could also have written an essay stating why his parents should let him go. When you are planning a persuasive writing, decide which form you think will work best.

Now look at Max's note and see why his parents have agreed to let him go to space camp.

Dear Mom and Dad,

1   I know we talked about space camp last night, and you said you weren't sure if it was a good idea. I'd really like you to know my reasons for wanting to go.

2   First of all, summer gets long and boring. Kids need something to do so we don't just lie around the house watching soap operas all day. Some kids—not me, of course—even get into trouble when they don't have something fun and challenging to do for a whole week.

3   Second, space camp will be very educational. When I started fifth grade, I had a little trouble remembering what I had learned in fourth. At space camp, I'll be learning all kinds of stuff about science and math. I'll have to do a lot of reading, too. Space camp will help me keep on top of my school skills.

4   And space camp will even be good for my health. I won't have time to sit around and pig out on candy and pop like I do now. I'll be eating healthy meals and getting a lot of exercise.

5   Also, at space camp I will meet a lot of really interesting people. You know, "good role models"—like astronauts, scientists, and even other kids who like to learn.

6   I promise I'll work hard to save money so you won't have to pay for all of it. I'll mow lawns for the neighbors and help Mrs. McGill walk her dogs. And I'll help you around the house as much as you want me to. I promise. I should be able to save half the cost of space camp by the end of July. (Think about it—this is a good lesson in managing money, too!)

7   So, you can see that sending me to space camp is a really good idea. It will give me something good to do with my time, keep my school skills sharp, keep me healthy, introduce me to some cool people, and help me manage money. Please sign the form and mail it in today.

8   I won't forget this, Mom and Dad. You're the greatest parents a kid could ever have. I'll write you from camp (I know you'll let me go) and tell you all about it.

Your loving son,
Max

What does Max want his parents to do?

_____

_____

_____

What facts does Max use to support his position? (First, go back and underline them in the letter.)

1. Paragraph 2: _____

_____

_____

2. Paragraph 3: _____

_____

_____

3. Paragraph 4: _____

_____

_____

4. Paragraph 5: _____

_____

_____

5. Paragraph 6: _____

_____

_____

Topic 8: Persuasive Writing

Directions: Your school recently canceled the school trip to the zoo. You decide to write a letter to the school principal, Mrs. Howell, persuading her to allow the school to go to the zoo.

Prewriting Activity

Directions: The activities and questions in this section will help you develop ideas for your persuasive letter to the principal. Write your ideas on the lines provided.

1. Why are you writing to Mrs. Howell, the school principal?

_____

_____

_____

_____

2. What are three main facts about why the school trip is a good idea?

Fact 1: _____

_____

Fact 2: _____

_____

Fact 3: _____

_____

3. Why do you think Fact 1 is important?

_____

_____

_____

4. Why do you think Fact 2 is important?

_____

_____

_____

5. Why do you think Fact 3 is important?

_____

_____

_____

6. What, exactly, do you want the principal to do?

_____

_____

_____

Writing Assignment

Directions: In this exercise, you will write a persuasive letter to Mrs. Howell, the school principal. In your letter, you will ask her to allow the school to take a trip to the zoo. Write your letter based on the information that you developed in the Prewriting Activity.

Be sure to use words that make your meaning clear. Also, make sure your letter is well organized and complete.

Use the checklist on this page to make sure your writing is the best it can be.

Writer's Checklist

✔ **I will earn my best score if:**

☐ My letter has a salutation (*Dear Mrs. Howell*).

☐ My letter explains why I am writing.

☐ My letter backs up my opinions with facts.

☐ My letter tells why those facts are important.

☐ My letter tells Mrs. Howell exactly what I want done.

☐ My letter has a complimentary closing (*Sincerely, Yours truly*).

☐ I use words that make my meaning clear.

☐ I do not use the same words over and over.

☐ I use different kinds of sentences.

☐ I make smooth transitions between paragraphs.

☐ I spell the words correctly.

☐ I use correct grammar, punctuation, and capitalization.

Directions: Write your persuasive letter on the following lines.

_____

_____

_____

_____

_____

_____

_____

_____

_____

_____

_____

_____

_____

_____

Lesson 27: Publishing Your Writing

You may simply want to share your story, report, or essay with friends and family. Or you might want your writing to be read by many more pairs of eyes. Perhaps you want to have a report published in the school newspaper. You might want to write a letter to the editor of your local newspaper telling about things kids are doing in your school. You might even submit a story to a magazine or website that publishes children's writing. These are just a few ways to have your work read by others.

TIP 1: **When sharing your writing with friends and family, think about how you can make it look special.**

This is a fun part of publishing your writing yourself. Just follow these five steps:

Step 1: **Make a cover page.**
When you have finished your writing, create a cover page that has the title and your name. You can also use colored paper or artwork to make it more attractive.

Step 2: **Type or write neatly on one side of each page.**
Be sure to revise and edit your writing. Then copy the final version on clean paper. Be sure that your handwriting is easy to read or that you haven't made any keyboarding errors.

Step 3: **Add artwork to help tell the story.**
Adding artwork to your writing will make it more interesting to read. You can use drawings, photos, or even a collage.

Step 4: **Add a back page.**
Add a blank piece of paper at the end. Use the same paper as the front cover.

Step 5: **Attach all the pages.**
Now you're ready to attach everything. An easy way is to staple the pages together along the left side. Place a staple at the top, middle, and bottom. Your "publication" is now finished.

Practice Activity

Directions: Choose something you have written, either in this book or for another school assignment. This should be a piece of writing you would like to share. Following the five steps listed on page 174, "self-publish" the piece of writing you chose.

TIP 2: Another way to share your writing is to have it published by a magazine or newspaper.

There are three basic steps in this process:

Step 1: **Select a publication.**
You may wish to focus on publications that accept work from young people. Your school librarian or a bookstore clerk may be able to help you. Many local newspapers have special sections that print writing by students. You may wish to see if your local paper has such a feature.

After you have selected a publication, read some of the articles. Ask yourself the following questions:

- What kind of writing does the publication feature? Are there stories, letters to the editor, and articles?

- Is your writing similar to the writing you see in the publication? Will your writing appeal to the publication's readers?

Step 2: **Send for the writer's guidelines.**
Before you send your writing to a magazine, you should write a letter asking for a copy of the magazine's writer's guidelines, or check for guidelines on the magazine's website. (For help with letter writing, see Lesson 24.) The writer's guidelines will tell you many things, including the following:

- the types of stories or articles the magazine publishes

- the number of words the story or article should have

- any special instructions for preparing your story or article

Step 3: **Submit your writing.**
If you decide to submit your writing, it is important to include a cover letter that tells what your article or story is about. (Again, for help with letter writing, see Lesson 24.) The checklist on the next page will help you make sure you have followed all the steps for submitting a work for publication.

Writer's Checklist

✓ **I have my best chance of being published when I have completed all of the following:**

☐ I have read a copy of the publication to learn more about it.

☐ I have written to the publication for a copy of its writer's guidelines, or checked the guidelines online.

☐ My writing follows the writer's guidelines and appeals to the readers of the magazine or newspaper.

☐ I have written a letter to the editor to send with my article or story. The letter has a greeting, a body, and a closing.

☐ My writing is well organized and complete.

☐ My writing stays focused on my topic.

☐ I have carefully revised and edited my writing.

☐ I have typed my writing, or my handwriting is easy for others to read.

☐ All the words are spelled correctly.

☐ The copy of my writing is neat and clean.

Unit 4 Practice: Additional Writing Prompts

For the following writing prompts, use a piece of scratch paper to generate and organize your ideas and plan your writing.

Directions: Write a fictional narrative about two people who find an animal that has escaped from the zoo. Be sure to include descriptions of the characters and setting, and develop a plot with an ending. Try to use dialogue in your story.

_____

_____

_____

_____

_____

_____

_____

_____

_____

_____

_____

_____

_____

_____

_____

_____

_____

Directions: Write an informational essay about a person or place in your town or city. You might write about a famous landmark, a very old tree, or a person who has had a lot of interesting experiences. Include as many important details as you can.

_____

_____

_____

_____

_____

_____

_____

_____

_____

_____

_____

_____

_____

_____

_____

_____

_____

Directions: Your family has decided to go on vacation to either the beach or the mountains. The members of your family disagree about where to go. Write an essay to convince your family to go to the place of your choice (either the beach or the mountains).

_____

_____

_____

_____

_____

_____

_____

_____

_____

_____

_____

_____

_____

_____

_____

Appendix

Spelling Log

Spelling Log

Keeping a spelling log will help you improve your spelling. Most of us are not terrible spellers. We just misspell the same words over and over.

Any time your teacher points out a misspelled word in your work, record the correct spelling in your log. Then spell the word correctly four times. This will help you to improve your spelling quickly.

Correct Spelling _____	Correct Spelling _____
_____ _____	_____ _____
_____ _____	_____ _____

Correct Spelling _____	Correct Spelling _____
_____ _____	_____ _____
_____ _____	_____ _____

Correct Spelling _____	Correct Spelling _____
_____ _____	_____ _____
_____ _____	_____ _____

Correct Spelling _____	Correct Spelling _____
_____ _____	_____ _____
_____ _____	_____ _____

Correct Spelling _____	Correct Spelling _____
_____ _____	_____ _____
_____ _____	_____ _____

Correct Spelling _____

_____ _____

_____ _____

Correct Spelling _____

_____ _____

_____ _____

Correct Spelling _____

_____ _____

_____ _____

Correct Spelling _____

_____ _____

_____ _____

Correct Spelling _____

_____ _____

_____ _____

Correct Spelling _____

_____ _____

_____ _____

Correct Spelling _____

_____ _____

_____ _____

Correct Spelling _____

_____ _____

_____ _____

Correct Spelling _____

_____ _____

_____ _____

Correct Spelling _____

_____ _____

_____ _____

Correct Spelling _____

_____ _____

_____ _____

Correct Spelling _____

_____ _____

_____ _____